D0336485

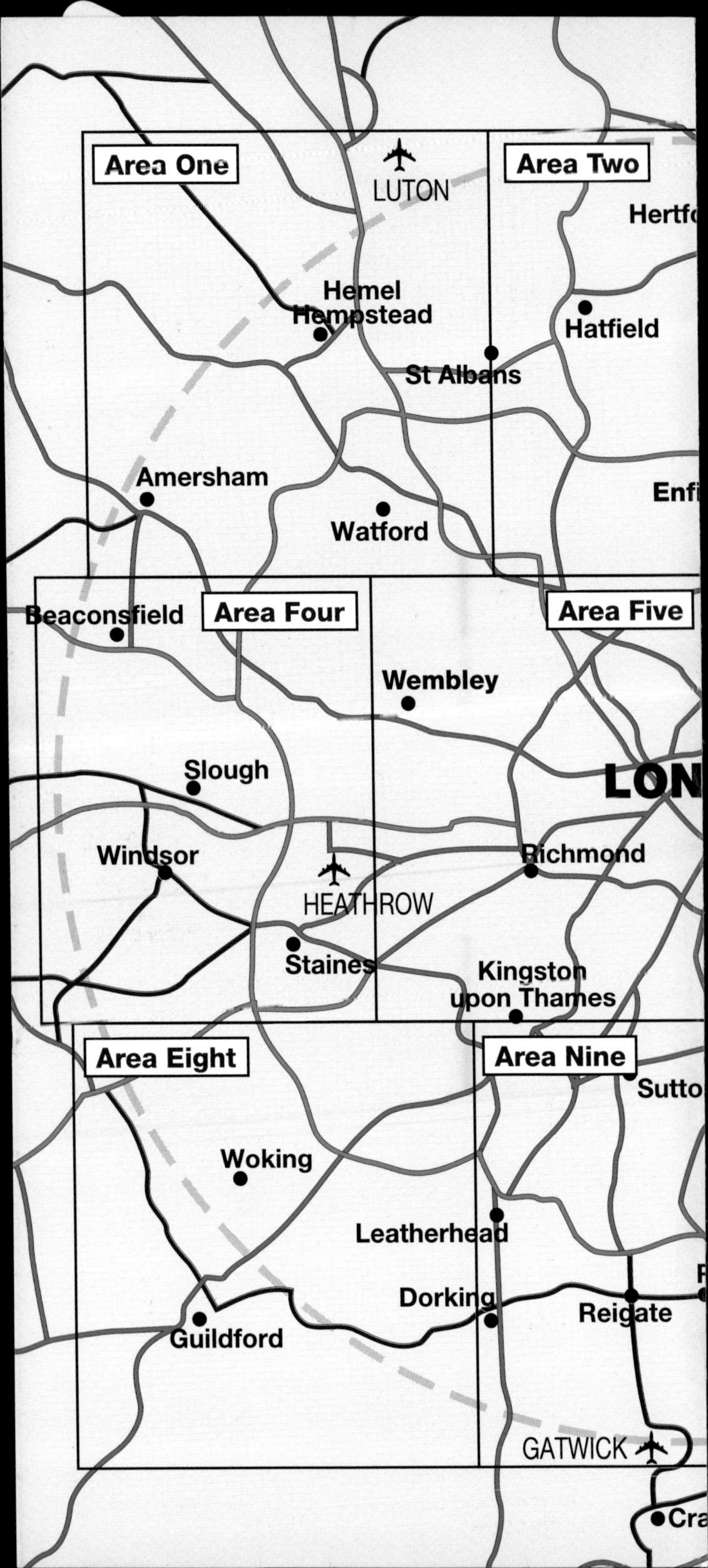

Area One
LUTON
Area Two
Hertf
Hemel Hempstead
Hatfield
St Albans
Amersham
Enfi
Watford
Beaconsfield
Area Four
Area Five
Wembley
Slough
LON
Windsor
Richmond
HEATHROW
Staines
Kingston upon Thames
Area Eight
Area Nine
Sutto
Woking
Leatherhead
Dorking
Reigate
Guildford
GATWICK
Cra

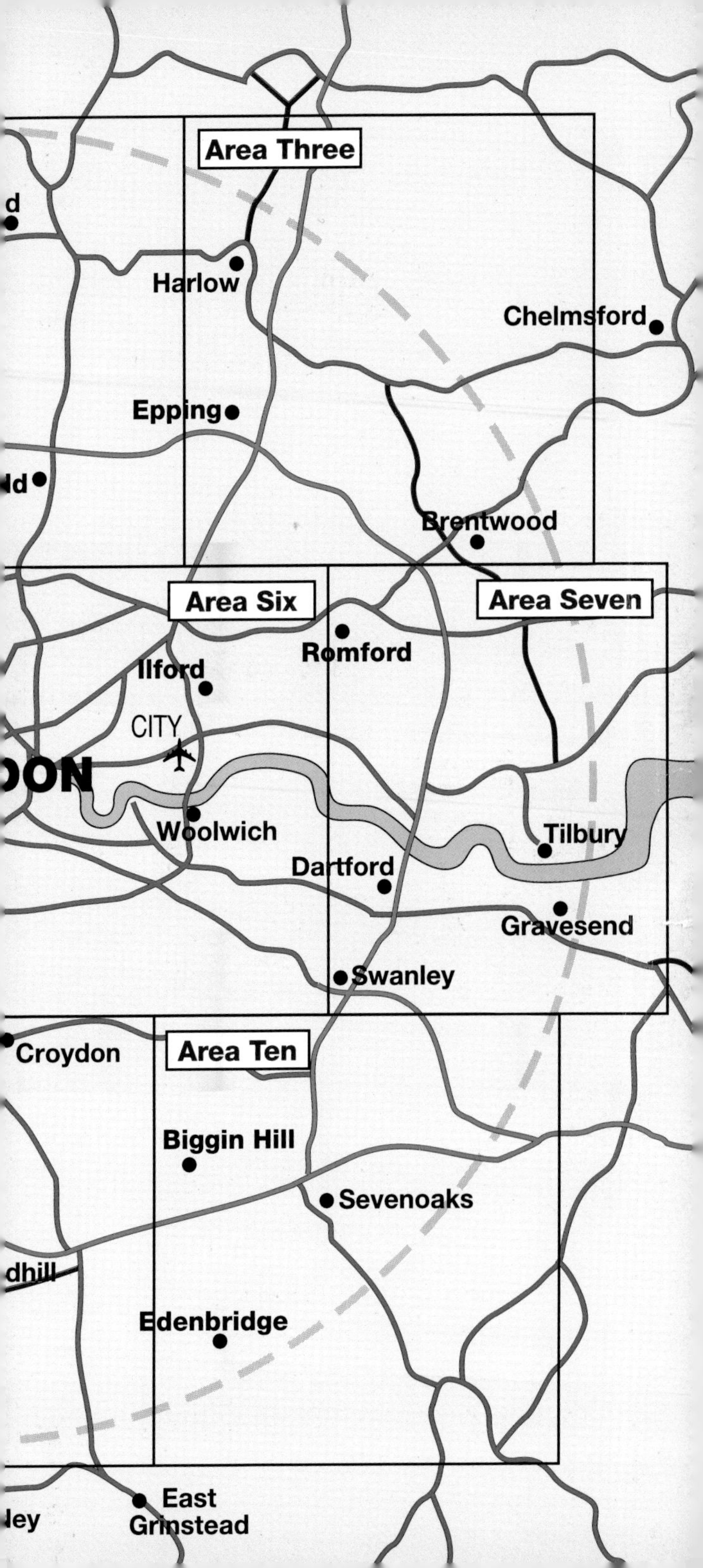

Area Three
d
Harlow
Chelmsford
Epping
ld
Brentwood
Area Six
Area Seven
Romford
Ilford
CITY
DON
Woolwich
Tilbury
Dartford
Gravesend
Swanley
Croydon
Area Ten
Biggin Hill
Sevenoaks
dhill
Edenbridge
East
Grinstead
ley

Ivinghoe
Whipsnade Park
A4146
Stocks Hotel
Ashridge
Tring
Aldbury
A4251
Berkhamsted
Berkhamstead
HEMEL HEMPSTE
A41
Little Hay
Boxmo
A416
Chartridge Park
Chesham
Chesham and Leyhill
A416
Amersham
Little Chalfont
A404
Chorleywoo
A404
A413
Harewood Downs
18
Rickmanswor
17

Stockwood Park (1973)

③

Stockwood Park, Luton, Beds LU1 4LX
Tel: 01582 413704 Fax: 481001

Green Fee: ① 18 Holes 6049 yds SSS: 69
Visitors: Any day Designer: Unknown

Pay & Play parkland course.

Driving Range: 24 Bays, Floodlit, 7.00am-9.00pm

Verulam (1905)

London Road, St. Albans, Herts AL1 1JG
Tel: 01727 853327 Fax: 812201 Pro: 861401
www.verulamgolf.co.uk

Green Fee: ② 18 Holes 6448 yds SSS: 71
Visitors: Weekdays Designer: James Braid

Parkland with water on three holes. Samuel Ryder was captain here in 1927 when he started the Ryder Cup.

West Herts (1890)

③

Cassiobury Park, Watford, Herts WD1 7SL
Tel: 01923 236484 Fax: 222300 Pro: 220352

Green Fee: ② 18 Holes 6488 yds SSS: 71
Visitors: Any day Designer: Morris/Mackenzie

Parkland. Set on a plateau, this course drys well.

Whipsnade Park (1974)

②

Studgam Lane, Dagnall, Herts HP4 1RH
Tel: 01442 842330 Fax: 842090 Pro: 842310
www.whipsnadeparkgc.co.uk

Green Fee: ② 18 Holes 6704 yds SSS: 72
Visitors: Weekdays Designer: Unknown

Pleasant views overlooking the Chilterns. Parkland course.

25 miles of Golf around London

Welcome to 25 miles of Golf around London. With over 300 golf clubs and over 20 separate driving ranges, it must be the capital golf city of the world.

Here golfing aficionados will find every type of golf (*excepting true links*) with prices that will suit everybody's pocket, as the Public Municipal (Pay & Play) courses are marvellous value. At the other end of the scale there are some quite memorable and magical experiences awaiting; some quite expensive while others are more reasonable.

Without doubt the area to the west of London features established courses of world renown: Wentworth; West Hill; Woking; Worplesdon; Sunningdale; The Berkshire; Camberley Heath and Swinley Forest compete with the best golfing areas in Great Britain.

One hundred years ago golf in London witnessed an upsurge in popular support, with over 50 clubs opening their doors in the 1890s. Three men dominated golf course design in the London area for some 40 years from 1890: Harry S. Colt, James Braid and J. H. Taylor. Over half of the 130 courses opening during this period were designed by these three gentlemen. The then new clubs were accommodated within ten miles of the city, by the 1990s they were being built outside a fifteen-mile radius. It is most interesting to note that the 1990s saw a similar renaissance in popular support for the game, with over 72 new courses opening in an attempt to satisfy the demand.

I hope you find this book useful in your search for new challenges and if you come across any I've missed (*I hope not*), then please let me know.

Good golfing

Roger Kidd

SEE HOW TO USE THIS GUIDE ON THE FRONT COVER INSIDE FLAP.

CONTENTS

25 MILES OF GOLF AROUND LONDON

Published by Kidd's Golf Guides
23 Belmont Road Wallington Surrey SM6 8TE

Course	Area No.
Limpsfield Chart	10
Lingfield Park	9
Little Chalfont	1
Little Hay	1
London Club	10
London Scottish	5
Loughton	3
Lullingstone	10
M	
Malden	9
Manor of Groves	3
Maylands	7
Merrist Wood	8
Mid Herts	2
Mid Kent	7
Milford	8
Mill Green	2
Mill Hill	2
Mill Ride	4
Mitcham	9
Moatlands	10
Moore Place	8
Moor Park	4
Muswell Hill	5
N	
Nazeing	2
New Zealand	8
Nizels	10
North Downs	9
North Middlesex	5
North Weald	3
Northwood	5
O	
Oakland Park	4
Oaks Park	9
Old Fold Manor	2
Orsett	7
P	
Pachesham Park	9
Panshanger	2
Park Wood	10

Course	Area No.
Pedham Place	10
Perivale Park	5
Pine Ridge	8
Pinner Hill	5
Porters Park	2
Potters Bar	2
Poult Wood	10
Priors, The	3
Purley Downs	9
Puttenham	8
Pyrford	8
Q	
Queenwood	8
R	
RAC	9
Redbourn	1
Redhill Golf Centre	9
Redhill & Reigate	9
Redlibbets	10
Reigate Heath	9
Reigate Hill	9
Richings Park	4
Richmond	5
Richmond Park	5
Rickmansworth	1
Risebridge	7
Riverside	6
Rochester & Cobham	7
Roehampton	5
Roker Park	8
Romford	7
Royal Ascot	4
Royal Blackheath	6
Royal Mid Surrey	5
Royal Wimbledon	5
Ruislip	4
Ruxley Park	6
S	
St. Clere's	7
St. Georges Hill	8
Sandown Park	8

Course	*Area No.*
Sandy Lodge	5
Selsdon Park Hotel	9
Shendish Manor	1
Shirley Park	9
Shooters Hill	6
Shortlands	6
Sidcup	6
Silvermere	8
Southern Valley	7
South Essex	7
South Herts	2
Stanmore	5
Stapleford Abbotts	3
Stockley Park	4
Stockbrook Manor	3
Stocks Hotel	1
Stockwood Park	1
Stoke Poges	4
Strawberry Hill	5
Sudbury	5
Sunbury	8
Sundridge Park	6
Sunningdale	8
Sunningdale Ladies	8
Surbiton	9
Surrey Golf & Fitness	9
Sutton Green	8
Sweetwoods Park	10
Swinley Forest	8

T

Course	Area No.
Tandridge	9
Thames Ditton	9
Theydon Bois	3
Thorndon Park	7
Thorney Park	4
Toot Hill	3
Top Meadow	7
Traditions	8
Trent Park	2
Tudor Park	2
Tunbridge Wells	10
Twickenham Park	5
Tyrrells Wood	9

Course	*Area No.*
U	
Upminster	7
Uxbridge	4
V	
Verulam	1
W	
Walton Heath	9
Wanstead	6
Warley Park	7
Weald Park	3
Welwyn Garden City	2
Wentworth	8
West Byfleet	8
Westerham	10
West Essex	2
West Herts	1
West Hill	8
West Kent	10
West Malling	10
West Middlesex	5
West Surrey	8
Wexham Park	4
Whipsnade Park	1
Whitehill	2
Whitewebbs Park	2
Wildernesse	10
Wimbledon Common	5
Wimbledon Park	5
Windlemere	8
Windlesham	8
Winter Hill	4
Wisley, The	8
Woking	8
Woodcote Park	9
Woodford	6
Woodlands Manor	10
World of Golf (New Malden)	9
World of Golf (Sidcup)	6
Worplesdon	8
Wrotham Heath	10
Wycombe Heights	4
Wyke Green	5

Area One

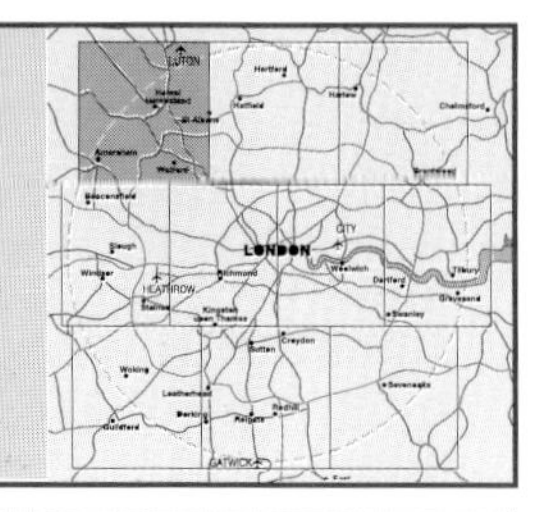

Aldenham (1975)

⑩

Church Lane, Aldenham, Watford, Herts WD25 8NN
Tel: 01923 853929 Fax: 858472

Green Fee: ② 18 Holes 6480 yds SSS: 71
Visitors: Any day Designer: Unknown

Parkland course with lakes. Has attractive copses of mature trees.

Aldwickbury Park (1995)

④

Piggottshill Lane, Harpenden, Herts AL5 1AB
Tel: 01582 765112 Fax: 760113 Pro: 760112
www.wwsl.co.uk/aldwickbury

Green Fee: ② 18 Holes 6352 yds SSS: 71
Visitors: Any day Designer: K. Brown/M. Gillett

Pretty and mature parkland course. Also has 9-hole course.

Ashridge (1932)

Little Gaddesden, Berkhamsted, Herts HP4 1LY
Tel: 01442 842244 Fax: 843770 Pro: 842307
www.ashridgegolfclub.ltd.uk

Green Fee: ④ 18 Holes 6547 yds SSS: 71
Visitors: Weekdays Designer: Sir Guy Campbell/ Major Hotchkin/Cecil Hutchinson

Excellent parkland course, challenging but fair. Regarded as one of the top 100 clubs in the UK.

Batchwood Hall (1935)

Batchwood Drive, St. Albans, Herts. AL3 5XA
Tel: 01727 844250 Fax: 850586

Green Fee: ① 18 Holes 6509 yds SSS: 71
Visitors: Any day Designer: J. H.; Taylor

Pay & Play parkland course.

Berkhamsted (1890)

The Common, Berkhamsted, Herts HP4 2QB
Tel: 01442 865832 Fax: 863730 Pro: 865851
www.linksnet.co.uk

Green Fee: ③ 18 Holes 6605 yds SSS: 72
Visitors: Any day Designer: Willie Park Jnr./ Harry S. Colt/James Braid

Heathland with heather and gorse. Long carries and natural hazards will test the best.

Boxmoor (1890)

18 Box Lane, Hemel Hempstead, Herts HP3 0DJ
Tel: 01442 242434

Green Fee: ① 9 Holes 4812 yds SSS: 64
Visitors: Any day Designer: Unknown

Challenging very hilly moorland course with sloping fairways divided by trees. Many fine views.

Bushey (1980) ③

High Street, Bushey, Herts WD2 1BJ
Tel: 020 8950 2283 Fax: 8386 1181 Pro: 8950 2215

Green Fee: ① 9 Holes 6120 yds SSS: 69
Visitors: Not Weds. Designer: Donald Steel

Parkland course. Although fairly open it has many fine oak trees.

Driving Range: 30 Bays, Floodlit, 9.00am-9.00pm

Bushey Hall (1886)

③

Bushey Hall Drive, Bushey Herts. WD2 2EP
Tel: 01923 222253 Fax: 229759 Pro: 225802

Green Fee: ② 18 Holes 6099 yds SSS: 69
Visitors: Any day Designer: Robert Clouston

Parkland with tree-lined fairways. Oldest course in Hertfordshire.

Chartridge Park (1990)

⑦

Chartridge, Chesham, Bucks HP5 2TF
Tel: 01494 791772
www.cpgc.co.uk

Green Fee: ② 18 Holes 5516 yds SSS: 69
Visitors: Any day Designer: John Jacobs

Parkland course set in idyllic surroundings. Has water hazard.

Chesham & Leyhill (1900)

Ley Hill, Chesham, Bucks HP5 1UZ
Tel: 01494 784541 Fax: 785506

Green Fee: ① 9 Holes 5296 yds SSS: 66
Visitors: Weekdays Designer: Unknown

Hilltop heathland course with easy walking. Tree-lined fairways.

Chorleywood (1890)

Common Road, Chorleywood, Herts WD3 5LN
Tel: 01923 282009 Fax: 286739

Green Fee: ② 9 Holes 5712 yds SSS: 67
Visitors: Weekdays except Tues. Designer: Unknown

Heath and woodland with fine views and natural hazards.

Harewood Downs (1907)

Cokes Lane, Chalfont St. Giles,
Bucks HP8 4TA
Tel: 01494 762308 Fax: 766869 Pro: 764102

Green Fee: ② 18 Holes 5958 yds SSS: 69
Visitors: Any day Designer: Unknown
Testing undulating parkland course with sloping greens.

Harpenden (1894)

Hammonds End, Redbourn Lane, Harpenden,
Herts AL5 2AX
Tel: 01582 712725 Fax: 712725 Pro: 767124

Green Fee: ② 18 Holes 6381 yds SSS: 70
Visitors: Mon/Tues/Wed/Fri Designer: Hawtree/Taylor
Easy walking parkland course.

Harpenden Common (1894)

Cravills Road, East Common, Harpenden,
Herts AL5 1BL
Tel: 01582 715959 Fax: 715959 Pro: 460655

Green Fee: ② 18 Holes 6214 yds SSS: 70
Visitors: Weekdays Designer: Unknown
Flat typical common course with good greens.

Ivinghoe (1967)

Wellcroft, Ivinghoe, Leighton Buzzard,
Beds LU7 9EF
Tel: 01296 668696 Fax: 662755

Green Fee: ① 9 Holes 4508 yds SSS: 62
Visitors: Any day Designer: R. Garrard & Sons
Testing parkland course with some water.

Little Chalfont (1981)

①

Lodge Lane, Little Chalfont, Bucks HP8 4AJ
Tel: 01494 764877 Fax: 762860 Pro: 762942

Green Fee: ① 9 Holes 5852 yds SSS: 68
Visitors: Any day Designer: James Dunne
Gently undulating parkland course surrounded by woods.

Little Hay (1977)

④

Box Lane, Bovingdon, Hemel Hempstead
Herts HP3 0DQ
Tel: 01442 833798

Green Fee: ① 18 Holes 6610 yds SSS: 72
Visitors: Any day Designer: Hawtree & Son
Pay & Play part parkland, part inland links.
Driving Range: 24 Bays, Floodlit, 8.00am-8.00pm

Redbourn (1971)

④

Kinsbourne Green Lane, Redbourn,
Herts AL3 7QA
Tel: 01582 793493 Fax: 794362

Green Fee: ② 18 Holes 6506 yds SSS: 71
Visitors: Any day Designer: H. Stovin
Testing parkland course.
Driving Range: 20 Bays, Floodlit, 7.00am-10.00pm

Rickmansworth (1937)

①

Moor Lane, Rickmansworth, Herts WD3 1QL
Tel: 01923 775278

Green Fee: ① 18 Holes 4493 yds SSS: 62
Visitors: Any day Designer: Harry S. Colt
Pay & Play undulating parkland course.

Shendish Manor (1988)

④

Shendish House, Apsley, Hemel Hempstead,
Herts HP3 0AA
Tel: 01442 251806 Fax: 230683

Green Fee: ① 18 Holes 5660 yds SSS: 67
Visitors: Any day Designer: Sir Henry Cotton/ Donald Steel
Pay & Play hilly parkland course.

Stocks Hotel (1993)

⑥

Stocks Road, Aldbury, Nr. Tring,
Herts. HP23 5RX
Tel: 01442 851341 Fax: 851253 Pro: 851491

Green Fee: ② 18 Holes 6804 yds SSS: 73
Visitors: Any day Designer: Mike Billcliffe
Beautiful parkland, part inland links course.

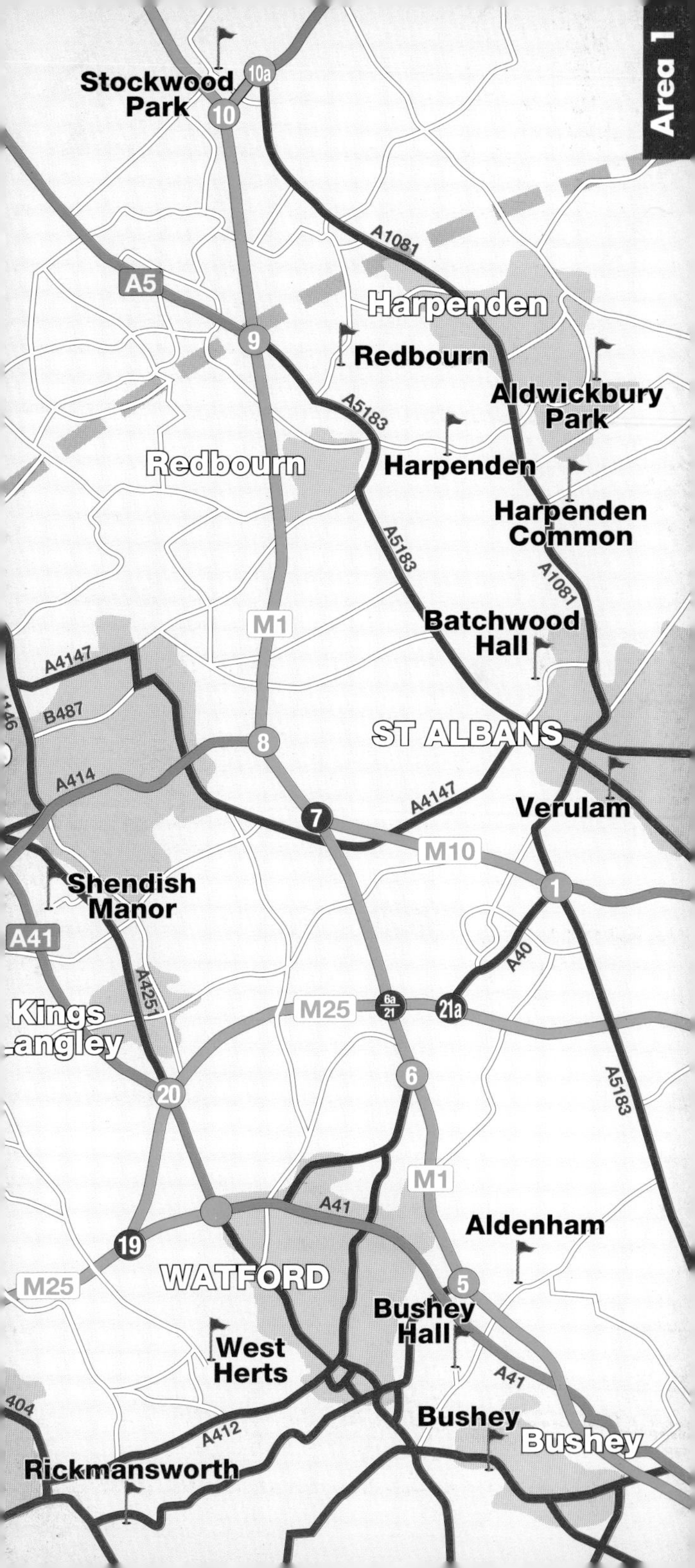

Area 1
Stockwood Park
10a
10
A1081
A5
Harpenden
9
Redbourn
Aldwickbury Park
A5183
Redbourn
Harpenden
Harpenden Common
A5183
A1081
M1
Batchwood Hall
A4147
B487
ST ALBANS
8
A414
A4147
Verulam
7
M10
Shendish Manor
1
A41
A40
A4251
Kings Langley
M25
6a
21
21a
20
6
A5183
M1
A41
Aldenham
19
M25
WATFORD
5
Bushey Hall
West Herts
A41
A412
Bushey
Bushey
Rickmansworth

Cuddington Golf Club

A very attractive parkland course with panoramic views of Surrey and London, Cuddington has recently re-laid all its greens to U.S.G.A. specifications.

This makes it an excellent test of golf and also means that apart from extreme weather conditions (snow) the course will never be closed. The recently refurbished clubhouse offers first class dining and bar facilities.

For societies and green fee enquiries please contact our secretary David Scott on:

Tel: 020 8393 0952
Fax: 020 8786 7025

Cuddington Golf Club

Banstead Road, Banstead, Surrey SM7 1RD

Area Two

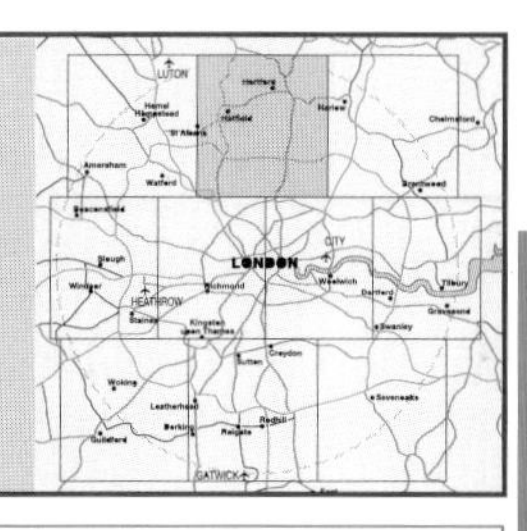

Arkley (1907)

Rowley Green Road, Barnet, Herts. EN5 3HL
Tel: 020 8449 0394 Fax: 8440 5214 Pro: 8440 8473

Green Fee: ② 9 Holes 6117 yds SSS: 69
Visitors: Weekdays Designer: James Braid

Highest spot in Hertfordshire. This parkland course has fine views.

Brickendon Grange (1964) ③

Pembridge Lane, Brickendon, Nr. Hertford, Herts. SG13 8PD
Tel: 01992 511258 Fax: 511411 Pro: 511218

Green Fee: ② 18 Holes 6394 yds SSS: 70
Visitors: Weekdays Designer: C. K. Cotton

Picturesque undulating parkland course. Very peaceful. Situated in grounds of country mansion.

Bridgedown (1994)  ⑩

St. Albans Road, Barnet, Herts. EN5 3HL
Tel: 020 8441 7649 Fax: 8440 2757 Pro: 8440 4009

Green Fee: ① 18 Holes 6626 yds SSS: 72
Visitors: Any day Designer: Howard Swann

Parkland course.

Briggens House Hotel (1988) ⑤

Stanstead Road, Stanstead Abbotts,
Ware, Herts. SH12 8LD
Tel: 01279 829955 Fax: 793685 Pro: 793742

Green Fee: ① 9 Holes 5586 yds SSS: 69
Visitors: Any day Designer: Unknown
An attractive parkland course set in the hotel grounds.

Brocket Hall (1992) ⑳

Brocket Hall, Welwyn Garden City,
Herts. AL8 7XG
Tel: 01707 390055 Fax: 390052 Pro: 390063

Green Fee: ③ 18 Holes 6616 yds SSS: 72
Melbourne: Parkland course with lots of water.
Green Fee: ③ 18 Holes 6823 yds SSS: 72
Palmerston: Woodland course, very undulating.
Visitors: Member's Guests Designer: P. Alliss/C. Clark

Brookmans Park (1930)

③

Golf Club Road, Hatfield, Herts. AL9 7AT
Tel: 01707 652487 Fax: 661851 Pro: 652468

Green Fee: ② 18 Holes 6473 yds SSS: 71
Visitors: Weekdays Designer: Hawtree & Taylor
Undulating testing parkland course.

Bush Hill Park (1895)

Bush Hill, Winchmore Hill, London N21 2BU
Tel: 020 8360 5738 Fax: 8360 5583 Pro: 8360 4103

Green Fee: ② 18 Holes 5760 yds SSS: 68
Visitors: Weekdays Designer: Unknown
Pleasant parkland course surrounded by trees.

Chadwell Springs (1974)

Hertford Road, Ware, Herts. SG12 9LE
Tel: 01920 461447 Fax: 466596 Pro: 462075

Green Fee: ② 9 Holes 6418 yds SSS: 69
Visitors: Any day Designer: J. H. Taylor

Moorland course situated on high plateau. Fine views. (Used to be called East Herts which was founded in 1898)

Area 2

Cheshunt (1976) ⑥

Park Lane, Cheshunt, Herts. EN7 6QD
Tel: 01992 629777 Pro: 624009

Green Fee: ① 18 Holes 6613 yds SSS: 71
Visitors: Any day Designer: Hawtree

Pay & Play. Well bunkered parkland course with some ponds.

Chingford (1888)

⑫

Bury Road, Chingford, London E4 7QJ
Tel: 020 8529 5708

Green Fee: ① 18 Holes 6342 yds SSS: 69
Visitors: Any day Designer: James Braid

Woodland course. Players must wear a red garment. Also home to Royal Epping Forest Golf Club.

Crews Hill (1920) ③

Cattlegate Road, Crews Hill, Enfield, Middlesex. EN2 8AZ
Tel: 020 8363 6674 Fax: 8364 5641 Pro: 8366 7422

Green Fee: ① 18 Holes 6224 yds SSS: 70
Visitors: Weekdays Designer: Arthur Lowe

Parkland course in country surroundings.

Dyrham Park (1963)

⑥

Galley Lane, Barnet, Herts. EN5 4RA
Tel: 020 8440 3361 Fax: 8441 9836 Pro: 8440 3904

Green Fee: ② 18 Holes 6428 yds SSS: 71
Visitors: Member's Guests Designer: C. K. Cotton

Parkland course.

Elstree (1984)

⑤

Watling Street, Elstree, Herts. WD6 3AA
Tel: 020 8953 6115 Fax: 8204 6390

Green Fee: ② 18 Holes 6556 yds SSS: 72
Visitors: Any day Designer: Unknown

Parkland course with water features.

Driving Range: 60 Bays, Floodlit, 7.00am-9.00pm

Enfield (1893)

Old Park Road South, Enfield, Middx. EN2 7DA
Tel: 020 8363 3970 Fax: 8342 0381 Pro: 8366 4492

Green Fee: ② 18 Holes 6154 yds SSS: 70
Visitors: Mon-Wed-Thur-Fri Designer: James Braid

Parkland course where Salmon's brook crosses 7 holes.

Forest Hills (1994)

Newgate St., Newgate St. Village, Herts. SG13 8EW
Tel: 01707 876825 Fax: 876825

Green Fee: ① 9 Holes 6440 yds SSS: 71
Visitors: Any day Designer: Mel Flanagan

Undulating attractive country course with USGA greens and lots of water hazards.

Hadley Wood (1922)

Beech Hill, Barnet, Herts. EN4 0JJ
Tel: 020 8449 4328 Fax: 8364 8633 Pro: 8449 3285
www.hadleywoodgc.com

Green Fee: ③ 18 Holes 6457 yds SSS: 71
Visitors: Weekdays Designer: A. MacKenzie

Parkland course. Pleasantly wooded with fine views.

Hanbury Manor (1990)

 ⑳

Ware, Herts. SG12 0SD
Tel: 01920 487722 Fax: 487692 Pro: 885000
www.linksnet.co.uk

Green Fee: ③ 18 Holes 7016 yds SSS: 74
Visitors: Member's Guests Designer: Jack Nicklaus II

Wonderful parkland course. Many large trees and lakes.

Hatfield London (1976)

Bedwell Park, Essendon, Hatfield, Herts. AL9 6JA
Tel: 01707 642624 Fax: 646187 Pro: 650431

Green Fee: ② 18 Holes 6279 yds SSS: 70
Visitors: Any day Designer: Fred Hawtree

Undulating parkland course. Very picturesque. Also has 18-hole Member's only course.

Area 2

The Hertfordshire (1995)

Broxbournebury Mansion, White Stubbs Lane, Broxbourne, Herts. EN10 7PY
Tel: 01992 466666 Fax: 470326 Pro: 441268
www.americangolf.com

Green Fee: ② 18 Holes 6388 yds SSS: 70
Visitors: Any day Designer: Jack Nicklaus II

Pay & Play parkland course.

Laing Sports (1982)

Rowley Lane, Arkley, Barnet, Herts, EN5 3HW
Tel: 020 8441 6051

Green Fee: ① 9 Holes 4178 yds SSS: 60
Visitors: Member's Guests Designer: Unknown

Parkland course.

Lamerwood (1996)

Codicote Road, Wheathampstead, Herts. AL4 8GB
Tel: 01582 833013 Fax: 832604
www.lamerwod.dircon.co.uk

Green Fee: ③ 18 Holes 6953 yds SSS: 72
Visitors: Any day Designer: Cameron Sinclair

Situated in the country. The course is set in 240 acres of mature trees and parkland.

Driving Range: 12 Bays, dawn to dusk

Lee Valley (1973)

Picketts Lock Lane, Edmonton, London N9 0AS
Tel: 020 8803 3611

Green Fee: ① 18 Holes 4902 yds SSS: 64
Visitors: Any day Designer: Unknown

Pay & Play parkland course, the River Lee providing a natural hazard.

Mid Herts (1892)

Gustard Wood, Wheathampstead, Herts. AL4 8RS
Tel: 01582 832242 Fax: 834834 Pro: 832788
www.mid-hertsgolfclub.co.uk

Green Fee: ② 18 Holes 6060 yds SSS: 69
Visitors: Weekdays Designer: Unknown

Commonland with heather and gorse lined fairways.

Mill Green (1994)

⑧

Gypsy Lane, Welwyn Garden City, Herts. AL7 4TY
Tel: 01707 276900 Fax: 276898 Pro: 270542
www.americangolf.com

Green Fee: ③ 18 Holes 6615 yds SSS: 72
Visitors: Any day Designer: P. Alliss/C. Clark

Parkland course surrounded by woodlands. Also has a 9-hole short course.

Mill Hill (1923)

④

100 Barnet Way, Mill Hill, London NW7 3ALF
Tel: 020 8959 2339 Fax: 8906 0731 Pro: 8959 7261

Green Fee: ② 18 Holes 6247 yds SSS: 70
Visitors: Any day Designer: Abercromby/Colt

Undulating parkland course with the holes separated by trees and shrubs.

Nazeing (1992)

 ⑨

Middle Street, Nazeing, Essex EN9 2LW
Tel: 01992 893915 Fax: 893882 Pro: 893798

Green Fee: ② 18 Holes 6598 yds SSS: 71
Visitors: Any day Designer: Martin Gillett

Meadowland course with ditches and ponds.

Driving Range: 15 Bays, dawn to dusk

Old Fold Manor (1910)

 ②

Old Fold Lane, Hadley Green, Barnet, Herts. EN5 4QN
Tel: 020 8440 9185 Fax: 8441 4863 Pro: 8440 7488
www.oldfoldmanor.co.uk

Green Fee: ② 18 Holes 6481 yds SSS: 71
Visitors: Any day Designer: Unknown

Attractive heathland course. Regularly holds county championships.

Panshanger (1975)

 ⑫

Old Herns Lane, Welwyn Garden City, Herts. AL7 2ED
Tel: 01707 333312 Fax: 390010 Pro: 333350

Green Fee: ① 18 Holes 6347 yds SSS: 70
Visitors: Any day Designer: Unknown

Pay & Play parkland course. Also has 9-hole par-3 course.

Porters Park (1899)

Shenley Hill, Radlett, Herts. WD7 7AZ
Tel: 01923 854127 Fax: 855475 Pro: 854366
www.porterspark.com

Green Fee: ③ 18 Holes 6313 yds SSS: 70
Visitors: Weekdays Designer: Unknown

Parkland course with a few water hazards.

Potters Bar (1924) ⑥

Darkes Lane, Potters Bar, Herts. EN6 1DE
Tel: 01707 652020 Fax: 655051 Pro: 652987

Green Fee: ② 18 Holes 6291 yds SSS: 70
Visitors: Weekdays Designer: James Braid

Undulating parkland course with water in play at two holes.

South Herts (1899) ④

Links Drive, Totteridge, London N20 8QU
Tel: 020 8445 2035 Fax: 8445 7569 Pro: 8445 4633

Green Fee: ② 18 Holes 6432 yds SSS: 71
Visitors: Weekdays Designer: Harry Vardon

Testing layout over rolling fairways, this parkland course had Harry Vardon as its first Pro. and Dai Rees since.

Trent Park (1973)

⑳+

Bramley Road, Oakwood, London N14 4UW
Tel: 020 8367 4653 Fax: 8366 3823

Green Fee: ① 18 Holes 6176 yds SSS: 69
Visitors: Any day Designer: Unknown

Pay & Play parkland course with 7 holes played across the Merryhills brook.

Driving Range: 57 Bays, Floodlit, 7.30am-10.00pm

Tudor Park (1937)

Clifford Road, New Barnet, Herts. EN5 5NY
Tel: 020 8449 0282

Green Fee: ① 9 Holes 3672 yds SSS: 58
Visitors: Any day Designer: Unknown

Pay & Play flat short parkland course.

Area 2

Welwyn Garden City (1922) ⑥

Manicotts, High Oaks Road,
Welwyn Garden CIty, Herts. AL8 7BP
Tel: 01707 325243 Fax: 393213 Pro: 325525

Green Fee: ② 18 Holes 6098 yds SSS: 69
Visitors: Any day Designer: Hawtree & Son

Undulating parkland course.

West Essex (1900)

④

Bury Road, Sewardstonebury, Chingford,
London E4 7QL
Tel: 020 8529 7558 Fax: 8524 7870 Pro: 8529 4367
www.westessexgolfclub.co.uk

Green Fee: ② 18 Holes 6289 yds SSS: 70
Visitors: Weekdays Designer: James Braid

Parkland course situated within the Epping Forest.

Whitehill (1990)

⑫

Dane End, Ware, Herts. SG12 0JS
Tel: 01920 438702 Fax: 438891 Pro: 438326

Green Fee: ① 18 Holes 6618 yds SSS: 72
Visitors: Any day Designer: Golf Landscapes

Very undulating parkland course.

Driving Range: 24 Bays, Floodlit, 7.00am-10.00pm

Whitewebbs Park (1932)

Whitewebbs Lane, Enfield, Middx, EN2 9HH
Tel: 020 83634454

Green Fee: ① 18 Holes 5782 yds SSS: 68
Visitors: Any day Designer: Unknown

Pay & Play flat wooded parkland course.

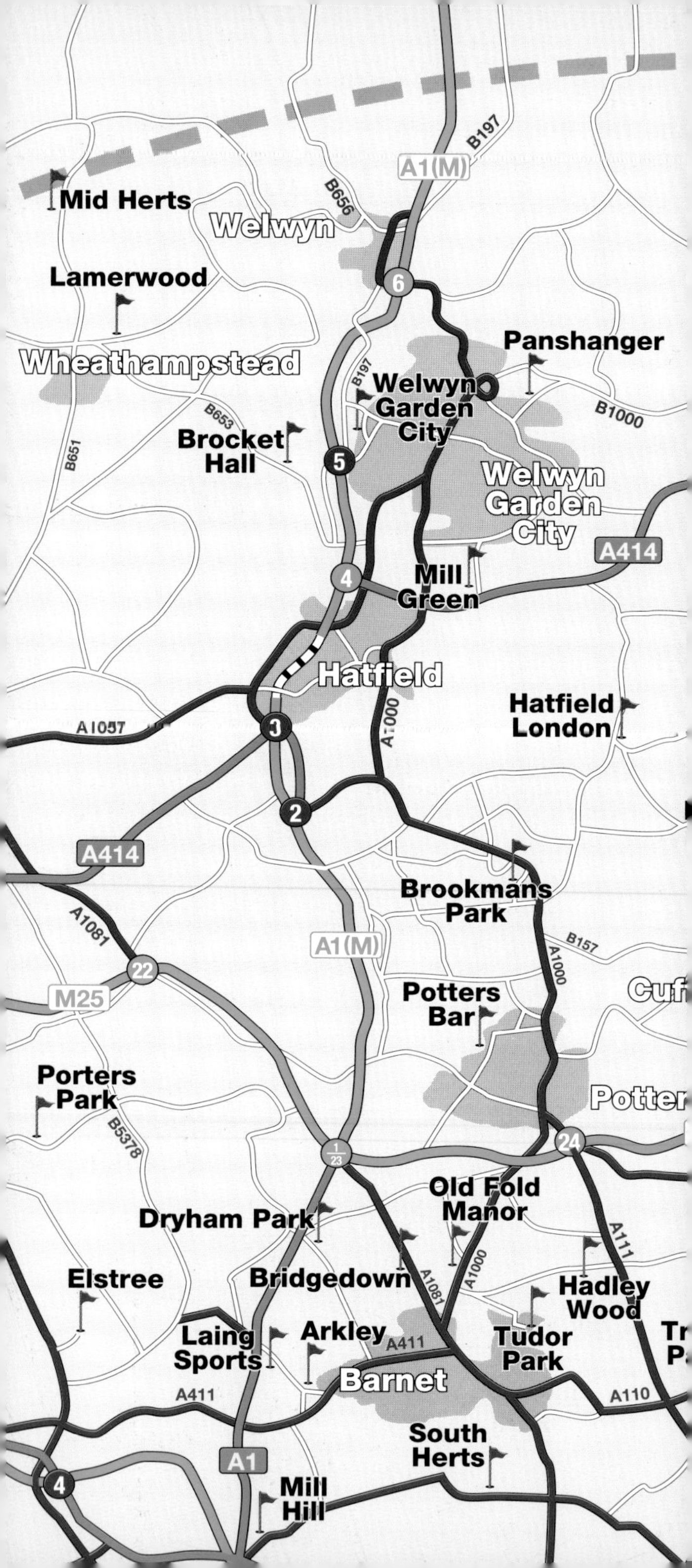

Mid Herts
Welwyn
B656
B197
A1(M)
Lamerwood
6
Panshanger
Wheathampstead
B197
Welwyn Garden City
B1000
B653
Brocket Hall
B651
5
Welwyn Garden City
A414
4
Mill Green
Hatfield
Hatfield London
A1057
A1000
2
A414
Brookmans Park
A1081
A1(M)
B157
A1000
22
M25
Potters Bar
Porters Park
B5378
Potter
24
1/23
Dryham Park
Old Fold Manor
Elstree
Bridgedown
A1081
A1000
A111
Hadley Wood
Laing Sports
Arkley
A411
Tudor Park
Barnet
A411
A110
South Herts
A1
4
Mill Hill

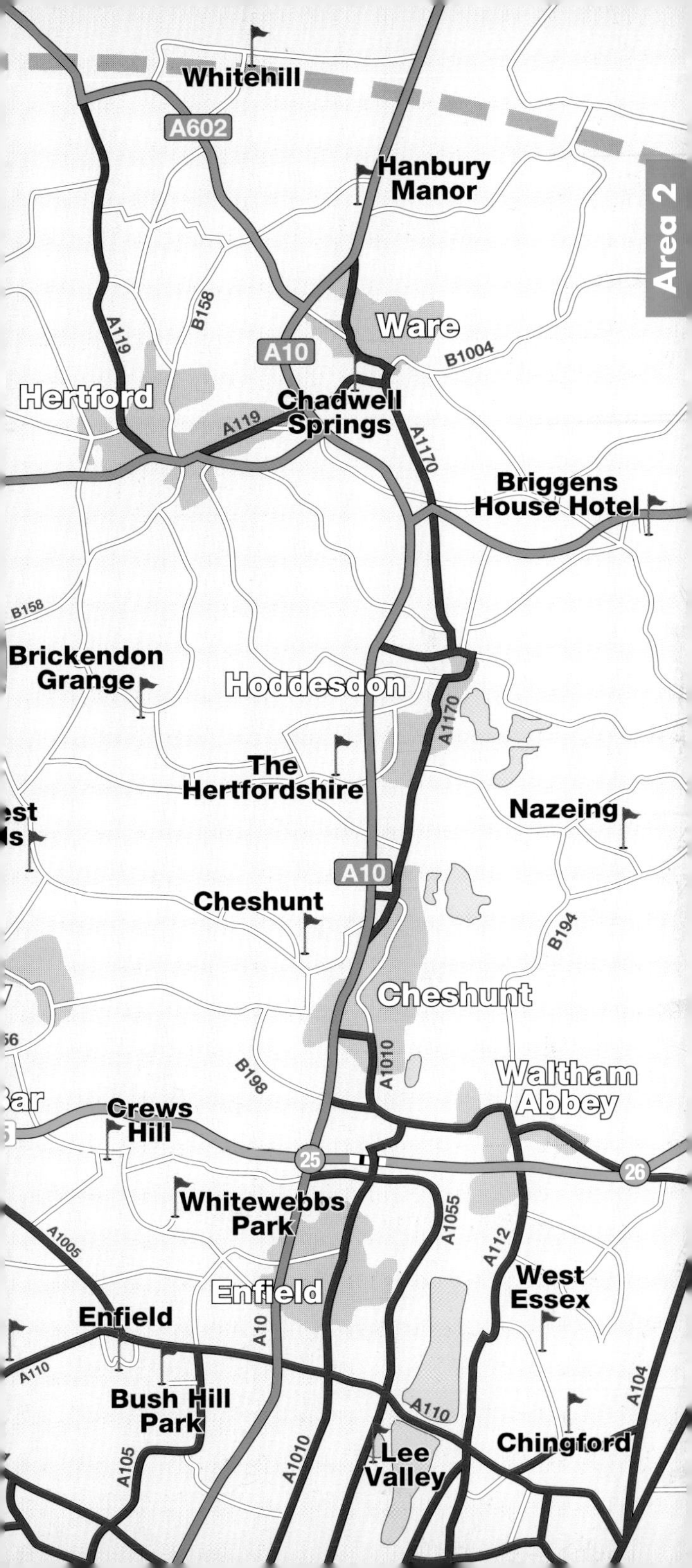

Area 2
Whitehill
A602
Hanbury
Manor
A119
B158
Ware
A10
B1004
Hertford
Chadwell
Springs
A119
A1170
Briggens
House Hotel
B158
Brickendon
Grange
Hoddesdon
A1170
The
Hertfordshire
Nazeing
A10
Cheshunt
B194
Cheshunt
A1010
Waltham
Abbey
B198
Crews
Hill
25
26
Whitewebbs
Park
A1055
A1005
A112
West
Essex
Enfield
Enfield
A10
A110
Bush Hill
Park
A110
A104
Chingford
A105
A1010
Lee
Valley

Area Three

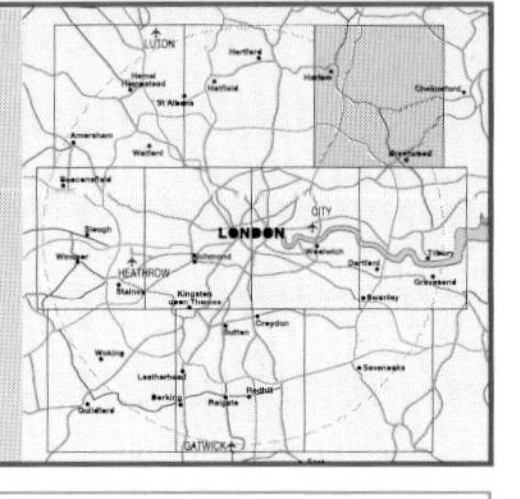

Abridge (1964)

Epping Lane, Stapleford Tawney, Essex RM4 1ST
Tel: 01708 688396 Fax: 688550 Pro: 688333

Green Fee: ② 18 Holes 6686 yds SSS: 72
Visitors: Any day Designer: Sir Henry Cotton

A quick drying parkland course. Easy walking with pleasant views.

Bentley (1972)

Ongar Road, Brentwood, Essex CM15 9SS
Tel: 01277 373179 Fax: 375097 Pro: 372933

Green Fee: ② 18 Holes 6709 yds SSS: 72
Visitors: Weekdays Designer: Alec Swan

Parkland course with ponds and ditches in abundance.

Cannons Brook (1962)

Elizabeth Way, Harlow, Essex CM19 5BE
Tel: 01279 421482 Fax: 626393 Pro: 418357

Green Fee: ② 18 Holes 6763 yds SSS: 73
Visitors: Weekdays Designer: Sir Henry Cotton

Splendid parkland course in wooded valley straddling the brook.

Epping Forest (1994)

Woolston Manor, Abridge Rd, Chigwell, Essex IG7 6BX
Tel: 020 8500 2549 Fax: 8501 5452 Pro: 8559 8272

Green Fee: ② 18 Holes 6408 yds SSS: 71
Visitors: Any day Designer: Neil Coles

Excellent wooded meadowland course. River Roding has to be crossed seven times.

Driving Range: 24 Bays, Floodlit, 7.30am-10.00pm

Area 3

Hobbs Cross (1996)

Hobbs Cross Road, Theydon Garnon, Epping, Essex CM16 7NQ
Tel: 01992 561661 Fax: 571471

Green Fee: ① 9 Holes 6010 yds SSS: 69
Visitors: Any day Designer: Martin Gillett

Pay & Play gently rolling meadowland course.

Loughton (1981)

Clays Lane, Debden Green, Loughton,
Essex IG10 2RZ
Tel: 020 8502 2923

Green Fee: ① 9 Holes 4480 yds SSS: 63
Visitors: Any day Designer: Unknown

Hilly woodland course with fine views.

Manor of Groves (1991) ⑥

High Wych, Sawbridgeworth, Herts. CM2 0LA
Tel: 01279 722333 Fax: 726972 Pro: 721486

Green Fee: ① 18 Holes 6228 yds SSS: 70
Visitors: Any day Designer: S. Sharer

Parkland course.

North Weald (1996)

⑩

Rayley Lane, North Weald, Essex CM16 6AR
Tel: 01992 522118 Fax: 522881 Pro: 524725

Green Fee: ① 18 Holes 6311 yds SSS: 70
Visitors: Any day Designer: David Williams

Meadowland course with seven lakes in play.

The Priors (1992)

⑦

Horsemans SIde, Tysea Hill, Stapleford Abbotts,
Essex RM4 1JU
Tel: 01277 373344
www.clubhaus.com

Green Fee: ① 18 Holes 5965 yds SSS: 69
Visitors: Any day Designer: Howard Swann

Meadowland course.

Stapleford Abbotts (1972)

⑨

Horsemans Side, Tysea Hill, Stapleford Abbotts,
Essex RM14 1JU
Tel: 01708 381108 Fax: 386345 Pro: 381278
www.clubhaus.com

Green Fee: ② 18 holes 6487 yds SSS: 71
Visitors: Any day Designer: Howard Swann

Meadowland course with water. Also 9-hole par-3 course.

Stockbrook Manor (1991)

Queens Park Avenue, Stock, Billericay,
Essex CM12 0SP
Tel: 01277 653616 Fax: 633063 Pro: 653616

Green Fee: ② 18 Holes 6905 yds SSS: 73
Visitors: Any day Designer: Martin Gillett

Also Driving Range and 9-hole, 5954 yd course, SSS 69.

Theydon Bois (1897)

Theydon Road, Epping, Essex CM16 4EH
Tel: 01992 813054 Fax: 813054 Pro: 812460

Green Fee: ② 18 Holes 5487 yds SSS: 68
Visitors: Any day Designer: James Braid

Woodland course with no par-5s. Forest-lined fairways.

Toot Hill (1991) ⑦

School Road, Toot Hill, Ongar, Essex CM5 9PU
Tel: 01277 365523 Fax: 364509 Pro: 365747

Green Fee: ② 18 Holes 6053 yds SSS: 69
Visitors: Any day Designer: Martin Gillett

Parkland course with lakes and a stream to be crossed 6 times.

Area 3

Weald Park (1994)

⑮

Coxtie Green Road, South Weald, Brentwood, Essex CM14 5RJ
Tel: 01277 375101 Fax: 374888 Pro: 375484
www.americangolf.com

Green Fee: ① 18 Holes 6285 yds SSS: 70
Visitors: Any day Designer: Reg Plumbridge

Parkland/Meadowland with wooded ponds and wildlife.

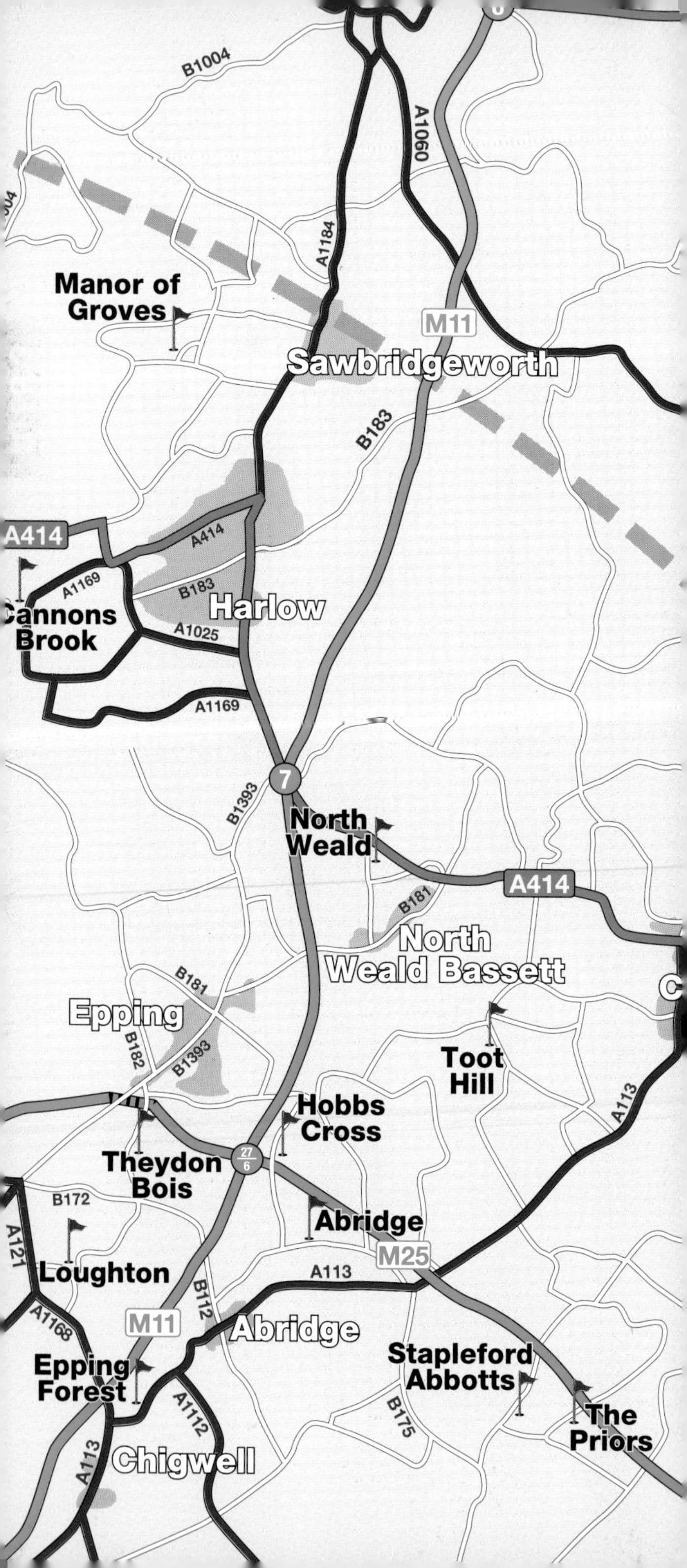

B1004
A1060
A1184
Manor of
Groves
M11
Sawbridgeworth
B183
A414
A414
A1169
B183
Harlow
Cannons
Brook
A1025
A1169
7
B1393
North
Weald
A414
B181
North
Weald Bassett
B181
Epping
B182
B1393
Toot
Hill
A113
Hobbs
Cross
Theydon
Bois
27
6
B172
Abridge
A121
M25
Loughton
A113
A1168
B112
M11
Abridge
Epping
Forest
A1112
Stapleford
Abbotts
B175
The
Priors
A113
Chigwell

A130
B1417
Area 3
B184
A1060
B184
A1060
A414
ping Ongar
A1016
B1002
A128
Ingatestone
Bentley
Stockbrook
Manor
B1007
A12
eald
ark
A129
Brentwood
A1023
A128

Area Four

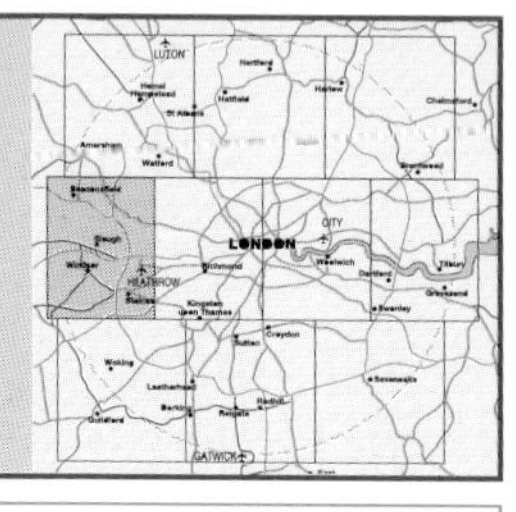

Ashford Manor (1898)

Footbridge Road, Ashford, Middlesex TW15 3RT
Tel: 01784 424644 Fax: 424649 Pro: 255940

Green Fee: ② 18 Holes 6352 yds SSS: 70
Visitors: Weekdays Designer: Unknown

Wooded parkland course.

Batchworth Park (1996)

London Road, Rickmansworth, Herts. WD3 1JS
Tel: 01923 714922 Fax: 710200
www.gch.co.uk

Green Fee: ② 18 Holes 6723 yds SSS: 72
Visitors: Member's Guest Designer: Dave Thomas

Parkland course with pleasant views.

Beaconsfield (1914)

Seer Green, Beaconsfield, Bucks. HP9 2UR
Tel: 01494 676545 Fax: 681148 Pro: 676616

Green Fee: ③ 18 Holes 6493 yds SSS: 71
Visitors: Weekdays Designer: Harry S. Colt

Charming and testing tree-lined parkland course.

The Buckinghamshire (1992)

Denham Court, Denham Court Drive,
Denham, Bucks. UB9 5BG
Tel: 01895 835777 Fax: 835210

Green Fee: ④ 18 Holes 6880 yds SSS: 73
Visitors: Weekdays Designer: John Jacobs

Undulating parkland course with mature trees, lakes & rivers.

Area 4

Burnham Beeches (1891)

Green Lane, Burnham, Bucks. SL1 8EG
Tel: 01628 661448 Fax: 668968 Pro: 661661

Green Fee: ③ 18 Holes 6449 yds SSS: 71
Visitors: Weekdays Designer: Harry S. Colt

Parkland course with some generous fairways.

Datchet (1890)

Buccleuch Road, Datchet, Slough, Berks. SL3 9BP
Tel: 01753 541872 Fax: 541872 Pro: 542755

Green Fee: ② 9 Holes 5978 yds SSS: 70
Visitors: Weekdays Designer: Unknown

Parkland course.

Denham (1910)

Tilehouse Lane, Denham, Bucks. UB9 5DE
Tel: 01895 832022 Fax: 835340 Pro: 832801

Green Fee: ③ 18 Holes 6451 yds SSS: 71
Visitors: Weekdays Designer: Harry S. Colt

Beautifully maintained parkland/heathland course.

Farnham Park (1974)

Park Road, Stoke Poges, Bucks. SL2 4PJ
Tel: 01753 647065 Fax: 643332 Pro: 643332

Green Fee: ① 18 Holes 6172 yds SSS: 69
Visitors: Any day Designer: Hawtree and Son

Pay & Play parkland course in pleasant surroundings.

Flackwell Heath (1905) ②

Treadaway Road, Flackwell Heath, Bucks. HP10 9PE
Tel: 01628 520929 Fax: 530040 Pro: 523017

Green Fee: ② 18 Holes 6211 yds SSS: 70
Visitors: Weekdays Designer: Unknown

Tree-lined undulating heathland course.

Gerrards Cross (1922)

Chalfont Park, Gerrards Cross, Bucks. SL9 0QA
Tel: 01753 883263 Fax: 883593 Pro: 885300

Green Fee: ③ 18 Holes 6212 yds SSS: 70
Visitors: Weekdays Designer: Bill Pedlar

Pleasant wooded parkland course.

Heath Park (Hol. Inn) (1975)

Stockley Road, West Drayton, Middlesex UB7 9BW
Tel: 01895 444232

Green Fee: ① 9 Holes 3800 yds SSS: 62
Visitors: Any day Designer: Neil Coles
Pay & Play hilly course with undulating greens. Ideal for beginners.

Hillingdon (1892)

18 Dorset Way, Hillingdon, Middlesex UB10 0JR
Tel: 01895 233956 Fax: 233956 Pro: 460035

Green Fee: ① 9 Holes 5490 yds SSS: 68
Visitors: Weekdays Designer: H. Woods/C. Stevens
Undulating parkland.

Area 4

Huntswood (1996) ②

Taplow Common Road, Burnham, Bucks. SL1 8LS
Tel: 01628 667144 Fax: 663145
www.huntswood-golf-club.co.uk

Green Fee: ① 9 Holes 5138 yds SSS: 64
Visitors: Any day Designer: Steve Morris
Pay & Play attractive wooded valley course. Fairly flat.

Iver (1986)

Hollow Hill Lane, Langley Park Road, Iver, Bucks. SL0 0JJ
Tel: 01753 655615 Fax: 654225

Green Fee: ① 9 Holes 6104 yds SSS: 70
Visitors: Any day Designer: David Morgan
Pay & Play parkland course.
Driving Range: 12 Bays, Dawn to Dusk

Lambourne (1992)

 ⑤

Dropmore Road, Burnham, Bucks. SL1 8NF
Tel: 01628 666755 Fax: 663301 Pro: 662936
www.gch.co.uk

Green Fee: ③ 18 Holes 6771 yds SSS: 73
Visitors: Weekdays Designer: Donald Steel
Parkland course.

Mill Ride (1990)

Mill Ride East, Mill Ride, North Ascot, Berks. SL5 8LT
Tel: 01344 891494 Fax: 886820 Pro: 886777

Green Fee: ③ 18 Holes 6807 yds SSS: 72
Visitors: Any day Designer: Donald Steel
Attractive blend of parkland and links.

Moor Park (1923)

⑤

Rickmansworth, Herts. WD3 1QN
Tel: 01923 773146 Fax: 777109 Pro: 774113
www.moorparkgolf.co.uk

Green Fee: ③ High: 18 Holes 6713 yds SSS: 72
West: 18 holes 5815 yds SSS: 68
Visitors: Weekdays Designer: Harry S. Colt
Two wonderful parkland courses with magnificent clubhouse.

Oakland Park (1994)

 ④

Three Households, Chalfont St. Giles, Bucks. HP8 4LW
Tel: 01494 876293 Fax: 874692 Pro: 874692

Green Fee: ① 18 Holes 5246 yds SSS: 66
Visitors: Weekdays Designer: Jonathan Gaunt

Beautiful meadowland course.

Richings Park (1996)

 ⑤

North Park, Iver, Bucks. SL0 9DL
Tel: 01753 655370 Fax: 655409 Pro: 655352
www.richingspark.co.uk

Green Fee: ① 18 Holes 6210 yds SSS: 69
Visitors: Any day Designer: David Williams

Parkland course with water in play at 8 holes

Driving Range: 12 Bays, Floodlit, Dawn to Dusk.

Area 4

Royal Ascot (1887)

Winkfield Road, Ascot, Berks. SL5 7LJ
Tel: 01344 625175 Fax: 872330 Pro: 624656

Green Fee: ① 18 Holes 5716 yds SSS: 68
Visitors: Member's Guests Designer: John H. Taylor
Heathland course situated inside Ascot racecourse.

Ruislip (1936)

⑥

Ickenham Road, Ruislip,
Middlesex HA4 7DQ
Tel: 01895 638081 Fax: 635780 Pro: 638835

Green Fee: ① 18 Holes 5571 yds SSS: 67
Visitors: Any day Designer: Sandy Herd
Pay & Play parkland course.
Driving Range: 40 Bays, Floodlit, 8.00am-10.30pm

Stockley Park (1993)

⑥

Uxbridge, Middlesex UB11 1AQ
Tel: 020 8561 6339 Fax: 8813 5655

Green Fee: ② 18 Holes 6539 yds SSS: 71
Visitors: Any day Designer: Robert Trent Jones, Snr.
Pay & Play hilly parkland course.

Stoke Poges (1908)

⑫

Stoke Park, Park Road, Stoke Poges, Bucks. SL2 4PG
Tel: 01753 717171 Fax: 717181 Pro: 717172
www.stokeparkclub.com

Green Fee: ⑥ 18 Holes 6770 yds SSS: 71
Visitors: Weekdays Designer: Harry S. Colt
Excellent parkland course with wonderful clubhouse.

Thorney Park (1992)

Thorney Mill Lane, Iver, Bucks. SL0 9AL
Tel: 01895 422095 Fax: 431307

Green Fee: ① 9 Holes 5668 yds SSS: 67
Visitors: Any day Designer: Grundon Leisure Ltd

Pay & Play parkland course.

Uxbridge (1947) ⑥

The Drive, Harefield Place, Uxbridge, Middlesex UB10 8AQ
Tel: 01895 231169 Fax: 810262 Pro: 237287

Green Fee: ① 18 Holes 5677 yds SSS: 68
Visitors: Any day Designer: Unknown

Pay & Play undulating parkland course.

Wexham Park (1979) ④

Wexham Street, Wexham, Slough, Bucks. SL3 6ND
Tel: 01753 663271 Fax: 663318 Pro: 663425

Green Fee: ① 18 Holes 5251 yds SSS: 66
Visitors: Any day Designer: E. Lawrence/D. Morgan

Gently undulating parkland course. Also 9-hole course.

Driving Range: 36 Bays, Dawn to Dusk

Winter Hill (1976)

Grange Lane, Cookham, Maidenhead, Berks. SL6 9RP
Tel: 01628 527810 Fax: 527479 Pro: 527610

Green Fee: ③ 18 Holes 6408 yds SSS: 71
Visitors: Weekdays Designer: Charles Lawrie

Parkland course adjacent to the River Thames with pleasant views.

Wycombe Heights (1991)  ⑧

Rayners Avenue, Loudwater, High Wycombe, Bucks. HP10 9SW
Tel: 01494 816686 Fax: 816728 Pro: 812862

Green Fee: ① 18 Holes 6253 yds SSS: 72
Visitors: Any day Designer: John Jacobs

Pay & Play parkland course.

Driving Range: 24 Bays, Floodlit, 10.00am-10.00pm

HIGH WYCOMBE
B474
A355
Oaklan Park
Wycombe Heights
Beaconsfie
A40
M40
Beaconsfield
3
2
Flackwell Heath
A4094
Winter Hill
Cookham
Lambourne
Farnham Park
B4447
Huntswood
Burnham Beeches
A355
A4094
Burnham
Stoke Poges
SLO
A4
River Thames
A308
7
M4
6
B3026
A308
Datche
B3024
B3022
A332
A330
B3022
B3011
B3034
Mill Ride
Royal Ascot
Ascot
B383
Virginia Water
A329
A329

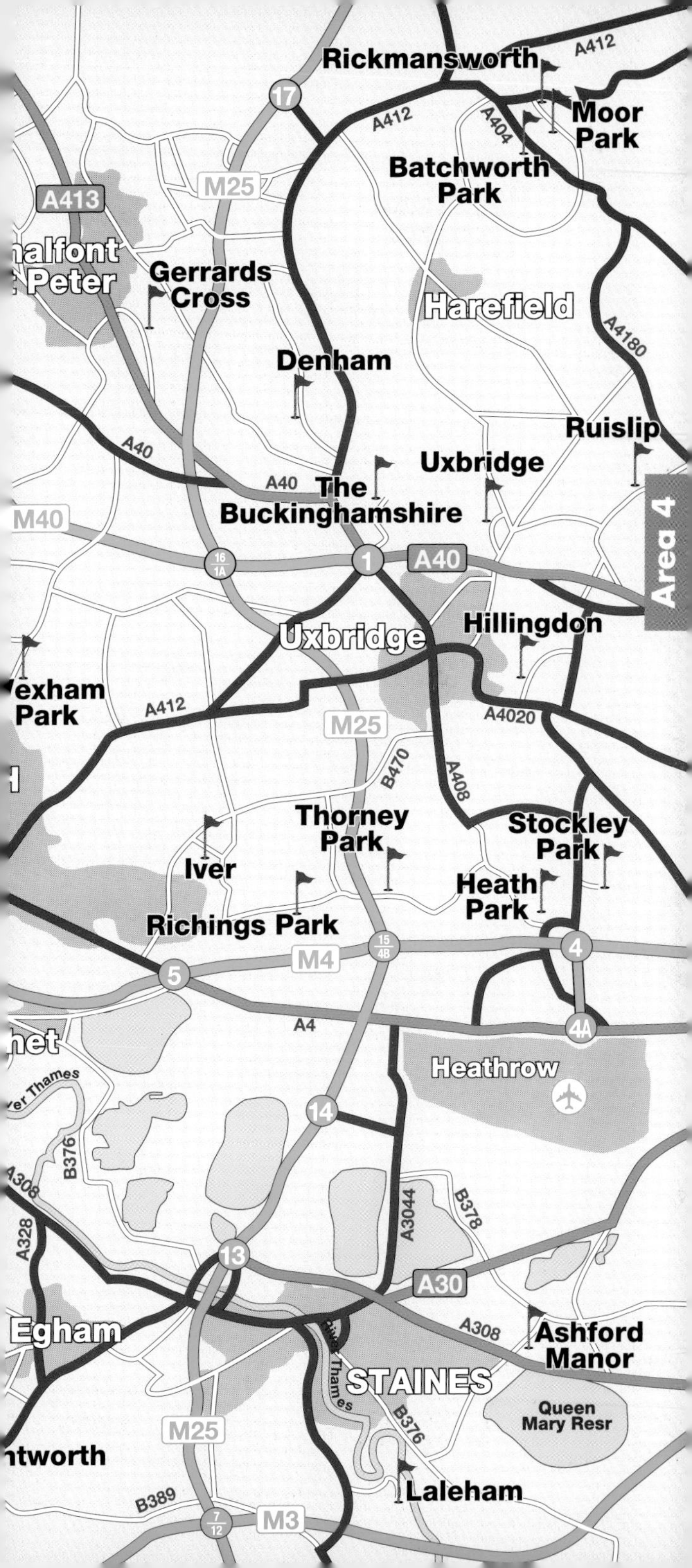

Rickmansworth
A412
17
Moor Park
A412
A404
Batchworth Park
M25
A413
halfont
Peter
Gerrards Cross
Harefield
A4180
Denham
Ruislip
A40
Uxbridge
A40
The Buckinghamshire
M40
16/1A
1
A40
Area 4
Uxbridge
Hillingdon
exham Park
A412
A4020
M25
B470
A408
Thorney Park
Stockley Park
Iver
Heath Park
Richings Park
15/4B
4
5
M4
A4
4A
het
Heathrow
ver Thames
14
B376
A308
A3044
B378
A328
13
A30
Egham
A308
Ashford Manor
STAINES
River Thames
B376
Queen Mary Resr
M25
ntworth
Laleham
B389
7/12
M3

Area Five

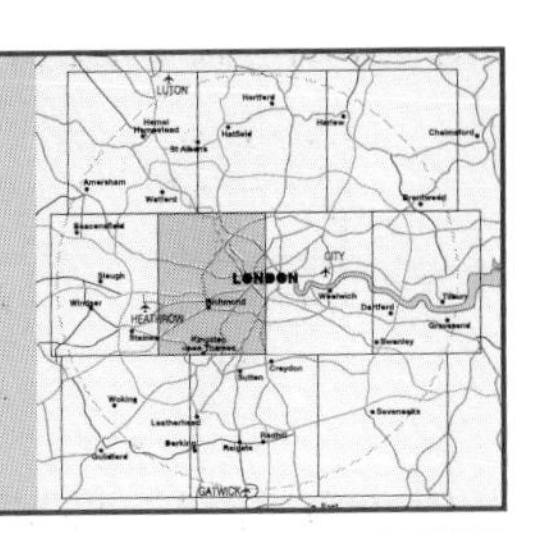

Airlinks (1984) ③

Southall Lane, Hounslow, Middlesex TW5 9PE
Tel: 020 8561 1418 Fax: 8813 6284

Green Fee: ① 18 Holes 6001 yds SSS: 68
Visitors: Any day Designer: P. Alliss/D. Thomas

Pay & Play part meadowland, parkland course.

Driving Range: 24 Bays, Floodlit, 10.00am-9.30pm

Brent Valley (1938)

Church Road, Hanwell, London W7 3BE
Tel: 020 8567 1287

Green Fee: ① 18 Holes 5446 yds SSS: 67
Visitors: Any day Designer: Unknown

Pay & Play parkland. The River Brent winds through the course.

Area 5

C & L Country Club (1991)

West End Road, Northholt, UB5 6RD
Tel: 020 8845 5662

Green Fee: ① 9 Holes 4562 yds SSS: 62
Visitors: Any day Designer: Patrick Tallack

Short Pay & Play parkland course. Ideal for beginners.

Central London (1993)

Burntwood Lane, Wandsworth, London SW17 0AT
Tel: 020 8871 2468 Fax: 8871 2468

Green Fee: ① 9 Holes 4468 yds SSS: 62
Visitors: Any day Designer: Patrick Tallack

Pay & Play parkland course. Ideal for beginners.

Ealing (1898)

①

Perivale Lane, Greenford, Middlesex UB6 8SS
Tel: 020 8997 0937 Fax: 8998 0756 Pro: 8997 3959

Green Fee: ③ 18 Holes 6216 yds SSS: 70
Visitors: Weekdays Designer: Harry S. Colt

Alongside the River Brent. Testing flat parkland course.

Finchley (1929)

Nether Court, Frith Lane, Mill Hill, London NW7 1PU
Tel: 020 8346 2436 Fax: 8343 4205 Pro: 8346 5086
www.finchleygolfclub.co.uk

Green Fee: ② 18 Holes 6356 yds SSS: 71
Visitors: Any day Designer: James Braid

Parkland wooded course.

Fulwell (1904)

Wellington Road, Hampton Hill, Middlesex TW12 1JY
Tel: 020 8977 2733 Fax: 8977 7732 Pro: 8977 3844

Green Fee: ② 18 Holes 6544 yds SSS: 71
Visitors: Weekdays Designer: D. Morrison

Part parkland, part meadowland easy walking course.

Grim's Dyke (1910)

Oxhey Lane, Hatch End, Pinner,
Middlesex HA5 4AL
Tel: 020 8428 4539 Fax: 8421 5494 Pro: 8428 7484

Green Fee: ② 18 Holes 5591 yds SSS: 67
Visitors: Weekdays Designer: James Braid

Gently undulating parkland course.

Area 5

Hampstead (1893)

Winnington Road, Hampstead, London N2 0TU
Tel: 020 8455 0203 Fax: 8731 6194 Pro: 8455 7089

Green Fee: ② 9 Holes 5822 yds SSS: 68
Visitors: Any day Designer: Tom Dunn

Undulating parkland course with mature trees.

Hartsbourne (1946)

⑤

Hartsbourne Avene, Bushey Heath, Herts. WD2 1JW
Tel: 020 8950 1133 Fax: 8950 5357 Pro: 8950 2836

Green Fee: ② 18 Holes 6385 yds SSS: 70
Visitors: Member's Guests Designer: Hawtree/Taylor
Lovely parkland course with ditches running through.

Haste Hill (1928)

The Drive, Northwood, Middlesex HA6 1HN
Tel: 01923 848300 Fax: 826485 Pro: 825224

Green Fee: ① 18 Holes 5797 yds SSS: 68
Visitors: Any day Designer: Unknown
Tree lined parkland course with stream running through.

Hendon (1903)

Ashley Walk, Devonshire Road, Mill Hill,
London NW7 1DG
Tel: 020 8346 6023 Fax: 8343 1974 Pro: 8346 8990

Green Fee: ② 18 Holes 6288 yds SSS: 70
Visitors: Any day Designer: Harry S. Colt
Testing parkland course.

Highgate (1904)

Danewood Road, London N6 4AH
Tel: 020 8340 3745 Fax: 8348 9152 Pro: 8340 5467
www.highgategolfclub.freeserve.co.uk

Green Fee: ③ 18 Holes 5985 yds SSS: 69
Visitors: Weekdays Designer: Unknown
Hilly parkland course.

Horsenden Hill (1935)

Woodland Rise, Greenford, Middlesex UB6 0RD
Tel: 020 8902 4555

Green Fee: ① 9 Holes 3264 yds SSS: 56
Visitors: Any day Designer: Unknown
Pay & Play hilly short course with wonderful views of London.

Hounslow Heath (1979)

Staines Road, Hounslow, Middlesex TW4 5DS
Tel: 020 8570 5271

Green Fee: ① 18 Holes 5901 yds SSS: 68
Visitors: Any day Designer: Fraser Middleton
Pay & Play heathland course with a variety of different trees.

Lime Trees Park (1982)

Ruislip Road, Northolt, Middlesex UB5 6QZ
Tel: 020 8845 3180

Green Fee: ① 9 Holes 5836 yds SSS: 69
Visitors: Any day Designer: Unknown

Pay & Play parkland course.

Driving Range: 18 Bays, Floodlit, 9.00am-10.00pm

London Scottish (1865)

Windmill Enclosure, Windmill Road, Wimbledon SW19 5NQ
Tel: 020 8789 7517 Fax: 8789 7517 Pro: 8789 1207

Green Fee: ① 18 Holes 5443 yds SSS: 66
Visitors: Weekdays Designer: Willie & Tom Dunn

Play is over Wimbledon Common. Red sleeved garment must be worn.

Muswell Hill (1893)

Rhodes Avenue, Wood Green, London N22 7UT
Tel: 020 8888 1764 Fax: 8889 9380 Pro: 8888 8046

Green Fee: ② 18 Holes 6432 yds SSS: 70
Visitors: Weekdays Designer: Unknown

Undulating narrow parkland course.

Area 5

North Middlesex (1928)

The Manor House, Friern Barnet Lane,
Whetstone, London N20 0NL
Tel: 020 8445 1604 Fax: 8445 5023 Pro: 8445 3060

Green Fee: ② 18 Holes 5625 yds SSS: 67
Visitors: Any day Designer: Willie Park, Jnr.

Short parkland course with tricky greens.

Northwood (1891)

Rickmansworth Road, Northwood,
Middlesex HA6 2QW
Tel: 01923 821384 Fax: 840150 Pro: 820112

Green Fee: ③ 18 Holes 6535 yds SSS: 71
Visitors: Weekdays Designer: James Braid

Parkland course with stream running through.

Perivale Park (1932)

Stockdove Way, Argyle Road, Greenford, Middlesex UB6 8EN
Tel: 020 8575 7116

Green Fee: ① 9 Holes 5334 yds SSS: 65
Visitors: Any day Designer: Unknown

Pay & Play parkland course ideal for beginners.

Pinner Hill (1927) ④

Southview Road, Pinner Hill, Middlesex HA5 3YA
Tel: 020 8866 0963 Fax: 8868 4817 Pro: 8866 2109

Green Fee: ② 18 Holes 6266 yds SSS: 70
Visitors: Weekdays Designer: J. H. Taylor

Hilly woodland course with marvellous view of London. The "London Eye" is visible from the course.

Richmond (1891)

Sudbrook Park, Richmond, Surrey TW10 7AS
Tel: 020 8940 4351 Fax: 8940 7914 Pro: 8940 7792

Green Fee: ② 18 Holes 6007 yds SSS: 69
Visitors: Any day Designer: Tom Dunn

Historic wooded parkland course adjacent to Richmond Park with 6 par-3 holes. Clubhouse is Georgian mansion.

Richmond Park (1923) ⑳

Roehampton Gate, Priory Lane, London SW15 5JR
Tel: 020 8876 1795 Fax: 8876 1354 Pro: 8876 3205
www.globalnet.co.uk/rpgc

Green Fee: ① Princes 18 Holes 5858 yds SSS: 69
Dukes 18 Holes 6036 yds SSS: 69
Visitors: Any day Designer: F. W. Hawtree

Two public parkland courses within the beautiful Richmond Park.

Driving Range: 18 Bays, Dusk to dawn

Roehampton (1901)

Roehampton Lane, London SW15 5LR
Tel: 020 8876 5505 Fax: 8392 2386 Pro: 8876 3858

Green Fee: ① 18 Holes 6054 yds SSS: 69
Visitors: Member's Guests Designer: Unknown

Tree-lined parkland course, not particularly long, and is more a thinker's than a long-hitter's course.

Royal Mid Surrey (1892)

Old Deer Park, Richmond, Surrey TW9 2SB
Tel: 020 8940 1894 Fax: 8332 2957 Pro: 8940 0459

Green Fee: ④ Outer: 18 Holes 6385 yds SSS: 70
Inner: 18 Holes 5544 yds SSS: 67
Visitors: Weekdays Designer: J. H. Taylor

Long playing parkland courses with flat fairways and cleverly placed bunkers.

Royal Wimbledon (1865)  ⑫

29 Camp Road, Wimbledon, London SW19 4UW
Tel: 020 8946 2125 Fax: 8944 8652 Pro: 8946 4606

Area 5

Green Fee: ③ 18 Holes 6348 yds SSS: 70
Visitors: Weekdays Designer: Harry S. Colt

Close to London. Delightful isolation walking along fairways amongst towering trees. Silver birch, heather and gorse abound.

Sandy Lodge (1910)  ①

Sandy Lodge Lane, Northwood, Middlesex HA6 2JD
Tel: 01923 825429 Fax: 824319 Pro: 825321

Green Fee: ③ 18 Holes 6730 yds SSS: 72
Visitors: Weekdays Designer: Harry Vardon

Inland links style course, unusual for area.

Stanmore (1893)

Gordon Avenue, Stanmore, Middlesex HA7 2RL
Tel: 020 8954 2599 Fax: 8954 6418 Pro: 8954 2646

Green Fee: ② 18 Holes 5860 yds SSS: 68
Visitors: Weekdays Designer: Unknown

Mixture of heathland, parkland and woodland holes. The 7th tee is the highest point in Middlesex.

Strawberry Hill (1900)

Wellesley Road, Twickenham, Middlesex TW2 5SD
Tel: 020 8894 0165 Fax: 8894 0165 Pro: 8898 2082

Green Fee: ① 9 Holes 4762 yds SSS: 62
Visitors: Weekdays Designer: J. H. Taylor

Easy walking parkland course.

Sudbury (1920)

Bridgewater Road, Wembley, Middlesex HA0 1AL
Tel: 020 8902 3713 Fax: 8903 2966 Pro: 8902 7910

Green Fee: ② 18 Holes 6282 yds SSS: 70
Visitors: Weekdays Designer: Harry S. Colt

Undulating parkland course.

Twickenham Park (1977)

Staines Road, Twickenham, Middlesex TW2 5JD
Tel: 020 8783 1698 Fax: 8941 9134 Pro: 8783 1698

Green Fee: ① 9 Holes 6076 yds SSS: 69
Visitors: Any day Designer: Charles Lawrie

Pay & Play parkland course.

West Middlesex (1891)

Greenford Road, Southall, Middlesex UB1 3EE
Tel: 020 8574 3450 Fax: 8574 2383 Pro: 8574 1800

Green Fee: ① 18 Holes 6119 yds SSS: 69
Visitors: Any day Designer: James Braid

Undulating parkland course.

Wimbledon Common (1908)

19 Camp Road, Wimbledon, London SW19 4UW
Tel: 020 8946 7571 Fax: 8946 7571 Pro: 8946 0294
www.linksnet.co.uk

Green Fee: ① 18 Holes 5438 yds SSS: 66
Visitors: Weekdays Designer: W. & T. Dunn

Shared with London Scottish. Wooded course with tight fairways. No bunkers. Red upper garment must be worn.

Wimbledon Park (1898)

Home Park Road, Wimbledon, London SW19 7HR
Tel: 020 8946 1250 Fax: 8944 8688 Pro: 8946 4053
www.surreygolf.co.uk

Green Fee: ③ 18 Holes 5492 yds SSS: 66
Visitors: Weekdays Designer: Wille Park, Jnr.

Short course around a lake with six par-3 holes, all of them quite challenging.

Wyke Green (1926) ①

Syon Lane, Isleworth, Middlesex TW7 5PT
Tel: 020 8560 8777 Fax: 8569 8392 Pro: 8847 0685

Green Fee: ② 18 Holes 6211 yds SSS: 70
Visitors: Mon. to Thurs. Designer: W. H. Tate

Fairly flat parkland course with 7 par-4s over 420 yards.

Area 5

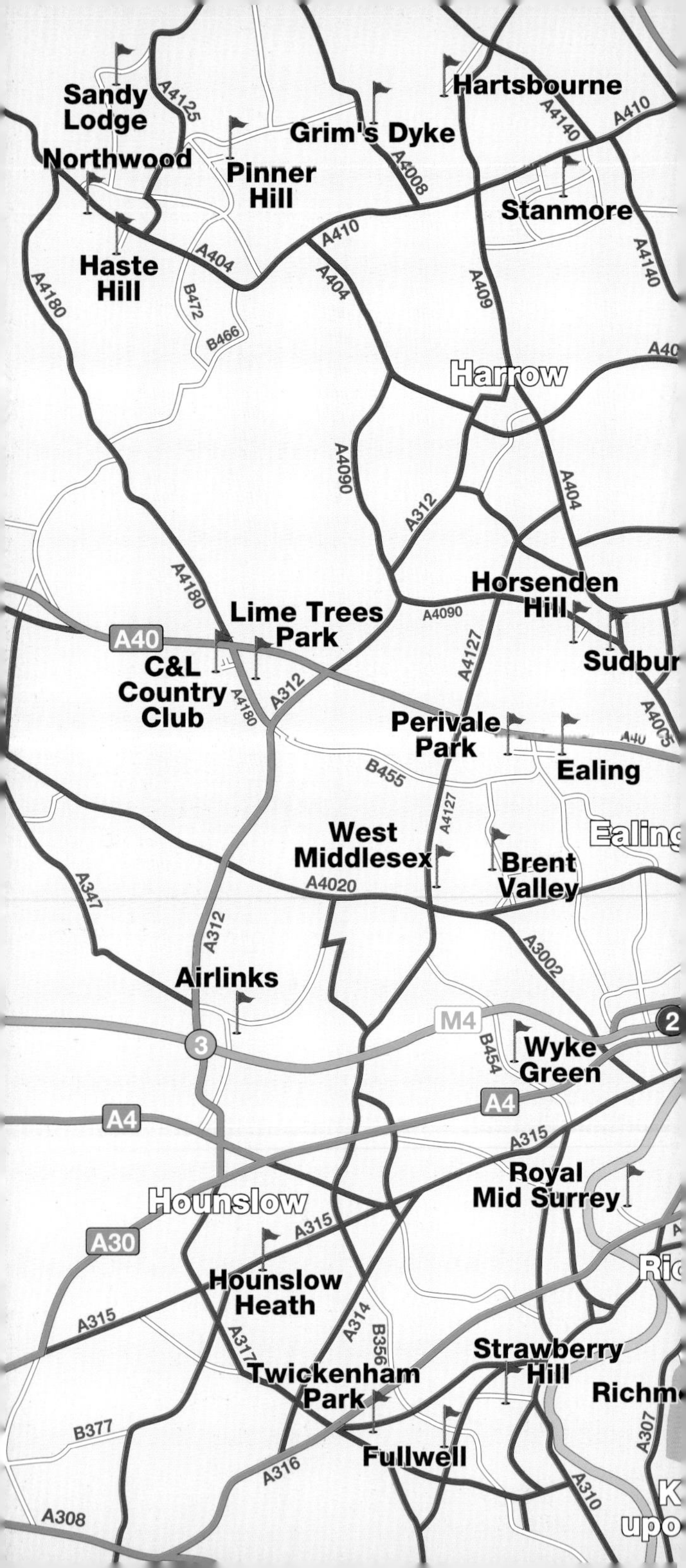

Sandy Lodge
A4125
Northwood
Pinner Hill
Grim's Dyke
A4008
Hartsbourne
A4140
A410
Stanmore
Haste Hill
A404
B472
B466
A4180
A410
A404
A409
A4140
Harrow
A4090
A312
A404
Horsenden Hill
A4090
A4127
Lime Trees Park
A40
C&L Country Club
A4180
A312
Perivale Park
Ealing
B455
A4127
West Middlesex
Brent Valley
A4020
A347
A312
A3002
Airlinks
M4
3
B454
Wyke Green
A4
A4
A315
Royal Mid Surrey
Hounslow
A30
A315
Hounslow Heath
A315
A314
B356
A317
Twickenham Park
Strawberry Hill
Fullwell
B377
A316
A308
A310
A307

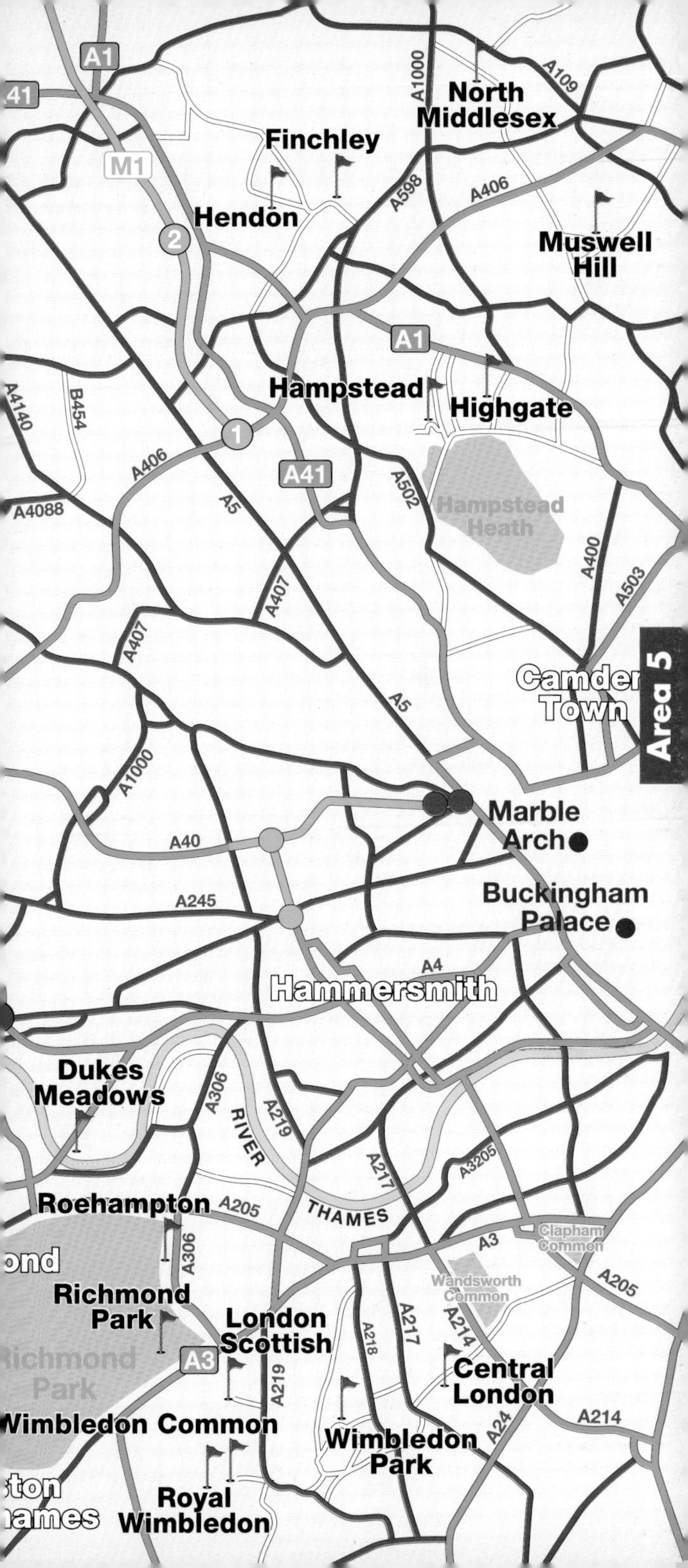

A1
A41
M1
2
1
North Middlesex
A1000
A109
Finchley
Hendon
A598
A406
Muswell Hill
A1
Hampstead
Highgate
A4140
B454
A406
A41
A502
Hampstead Heath
A4088
A5
A407
A400
A503
A407
Camden Town
Area 5
A5
A1000
Marble Arch
A40
A245
Buckingham Palace
A4
Hammersmith
Dukes Meadows
A306
River
A219
A217
A3205
Thames
Roehampton
A205
Clapham Common
A3
A205
A306
Wandsworth Common
Richmond Park
A218
A217
A214
London Scottish
A3
Richmond Park
A219
Central London
Wimbledon Common
A214
A24
Wimbledon Park
Royal Wimbledon

Area Six

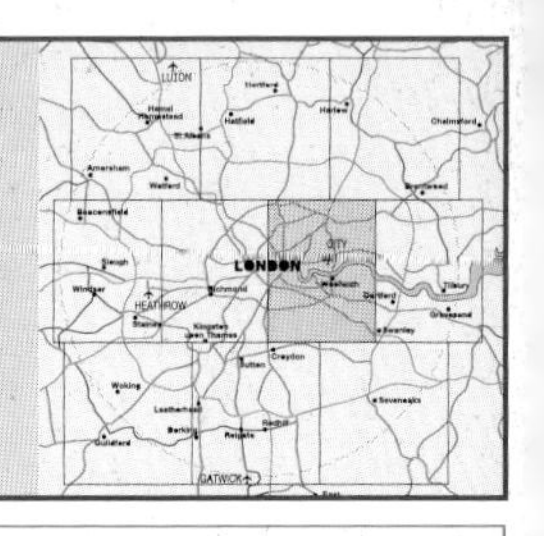

Aquarius (1913)

Marmora Road, Honor Oak, London SE22 0RY
Tel: 020 8693 1626

Green Fee: ① 9 Holes 5246 yds SSS: 66
Visitors: Member's Guests Designer: Unknown

Course laid out on two levels around and over covered reservoir.

Beckenham Place Park (1907)

Beckenham Hill Road, Beckenham,
Kent BR3 2BP
Tel: 020 8650 2292 Fax: 8663 1201

Green Fee: ① 18 Holes 5722 yds SSS: 69
Visitors: Any day Designer: Donald Steel

Club house is in "the Mansion House" built in 1773. Parkland course with lots of mature trees.

Selsdon Park Hotel & Golf Course

Addington Road, Sanderstead, South Croydon CR2 8YA
Telephone: 020 8657 8811 Facsimile: 020 8657 6171

Set high on the rolling hills of the Surrey Downs, the Selsdon Park Hotel combines the ancient virtues of hospitality and courtesy with the modern attributes of efficiency and friendliness. An outstanding asset to the Selsdon Park Hotel is the 18-hole championship golf course laid out in 1929 by five times British Open golf champion, J. H. Taylor. Originally cut out of the thick forest which clothes this part of the Surrey hills, the course has been extended over the years, but the layout remains substantially as it was over seventy years ago.

Summer	(round)	£27.50 pp	£35.00 pp
	(day)	£40.00 pp	£60.00 pp
Winter	(round)	£22.50 pp	£27.50 pp
	(day)	£30.00 pp	£50.00 pp

Putting Green, Driving Range and Practice Area available.

Societies and visitors welcome seven days a week

For more information please call the Golf Manager, *Caroline Screene*, direct on

Bexleyheath (1907)

Mount Road, Bexleyheath, Kent DA6 8JS
Tel: 020 8303 6951

Green Fee: ② 9 Holes 5239 yds SSS: 66
Visitors: Weekdays Designer: Unknown

Undulating 9-hole course.

Chigwell (1925)

High Street, Chigwell, Essex IG7 5BH
Tel: 020 8500 2059 Fax: 8501 3410 Pro: 8500 2384

Green Fee: ③ 18 Holes 6279 yds SSS: 70
Visitors: Weekdays Designer: F. Hawtree/J. H. Taylor

Very pretty undulating parkland course.

Chislehurst (1894)

Camden Place, Chislehurst, Kent BR7 5HJ
Tel: 020 8467 3055 Fax: 8295 0874 Pro: 8467 6798

Green Fee: ② 18 Holes 5106 yds SSS: 65
Visitors: Weekdays Designer: Tom Dunn

Parkland course with easy walking. Marvellous historic clubhouse.

Cray Valley (1972)

Sandy Lane, St. Paul's Cray, Orpington, Kent BR5 3HY
Tel: 01689 837909 Fax: 891428
www.americangolf.co.uk

Green Fee: ① 18 Holes 5669 yds SSS: 67
Visitors: Any day Designer: Unknown

Pay & Play. Attractive open parkland course with two man-made lakes.

Dulwich & Sydenham (1894)  ④

Grange Lane, College Road, Dulwich, London SE21 7LH
Tel: 020 8693 3961 Fax: 8693 2481 Pro: 8693 8491

Green Fee: ② 18 Holes 6051 yds SSS: 69
Visitors: Weekdays Designer: Unknown

Attractive parkland course adjacent to Dulwich College. Superb panoramic views over London.

Eltham Warren (1890)

Bexley Road, Eltham London SE9 2PE
Tel: 020 8850 1166 Pro: 8859 7909

Green Fee: ② 9 Holes 5840 yds SSS: 68
Visitors: Weekdays Designer: James Braid

Parkland course with lots of mature trees. Although not long straight driving essential. Easy walking.

Fairlop Waters (1987)

Forest Road, Barkingside, Ilford, Essex IG6 3HN
Tel: 020 8500 9911 Pro: 8501 1881

Green Fee: ① 18 Holes 6281 yds SSS: 70
Visitors: Any day Designer: John Jacobs

Pay & Play. This flat heathland course is ideal for all standards of players.

Driving Range: 36 Bays, Floodlit, 7.00am-9.00pm

Hainault Forest (1912) 

⑳+

Romford Road, Chigwell, Essex IG7 4QW
Tel: 020 8500 2131 Fax: 8501 5196
www.essexgolfcentre.com

Green Fee: ① Lower 18 Holes 6545 yds SSS: 72
Upper 18 Holes 5886 yds SSS: 68
Visitors: Any day Designer: F. Hawtree/J. H. Taylor

Pay & Play. Very popular undulating woodland course in what is left of the forest.

Ilford (1907)

291 Wanstead Park Road, Ilford, Essex IG1 3TR
Tel: 020 8554 2930 Pro: 8554 0094

Green Fee: ① 18 Holes 5299 yds SSS: 66
Visitors: Any day Designer: Unknown

Flat parkland with the River Roding running through the course.

Riverside (1993)

Summerton Way, Thamesmead, London SE28 8PP
Tel: 020 8310 7975

Green Fee: ① 9 Holes 5462 yds SSS: 66
Visitors: Weekdays Designer: Eddie Springham

Pay & Play parkland course on banks of River Thames with many water hazards.

Driving Range: 30 Bays, Floodlit, 7.30am-11.00pm

Royal Blackheath (1608) 

Court Road, Eltham, London SE9 5AF
Tel: 020 8850 1795 Fax: 8859 0150 Pro: 8850 1763
www.rbgc.com

Green Fee: ③ 18 Holes 6219 yds SSS: 70
Visitors: Any day Designer: James Braid

A pleasant parkland course with a clubhouse that dates back to the 17th Century. Many great trees survive. Listed as the oldest club in England

Ruxley Park (1975) 

Sandy Lane, St. Paul's Cray, Orpington, Kent BR5 3HY
Tel: 01689 871490 Fax: 891428
www.americangolf.com

Green Fee: ① 18 Holes 5712 yds SSS: 68
Visitors: Any day Designer: Peter Bevan

Pay & Play parkland course with 9-hole par-3.

Driving Range: 25 Bays, Floodlit, 7.00am-10.00pm

Shooters Hill (1903)

Lowood, Eaglefield Road, London SE18 3DA
Tel: 020 8854 1216 Fax: 8854 0469 Pro: 8854 0073

Green Fee: ② 18 Holes 5721 yds SSS: 68
Visitors: Weekdays Designer: Willie Park

Very hilly parkland/woodland course.

Shortlands (1894)

Meadow Road, Shortlands, Bromley,
Kent BR2 0PB
Tel: 020 8460 2471 Fax: 8460 8828 Pro: 8464 6182

Green Fee: ① 9 Holes 5261 yds SSS: 66
Visitors: Member's Guests Designer: Unknown

9-hole course adjacent to Shortlands Railway Station.

Sidcup (1891)

7 Hurst Road, Sidcup, Kent DA15 9AE
Tel: 020 8300 2150 Fax: 8300 2150 Pro: 8309 0679

Green Fee: ① 9 Holes 5722 yds SSS: 68
Visitors: Weekdays Designer: Unknown

9-hole parkland course with two lakes and a river running through and coming into play on 7 of the 9 holes.

Sundridge Park (1901)

Garden Road, Bromley, Kent BR1 3NE
Tel: 020 8460 0278 Fax: 8289 3050 Pro: 8460 5540

Green Fee: ④ 18 Holes East: 6538 yds SSS: 71
18 Holes West: 6019 yds SSS: 69
Visitors: Weekdays Designer: Willie Park

Commanding views of City of London, whilst the West course offers delightful views of Kent. Clubhouse is a wonderful 18th Century mansion.

Area 6

Wanstead (1893)

Overton Drive, Wanstead, London E11 2LW
Tel: 020 8989 3938 Fax: 8532 9138 Pro: 8989 9876

Green Fee: ② 18 Holes 6262 yds SSS: 69
Visitors: Weekdays Designer: James Braid

Delightful established parkland course with large lake and many trees.

Woodford (1890)

2 Sunset Avenue, Woodford Green, Essex IG8 0ST
Tel: 020 8504 3330 Fax: 8504 3390 Pro: 8504 4254

Green Fee: ① 9 Holes 5876 yds SSS: 68
Visitors: Any day Designer: Tom Dunn

Some wonderful views from this undulating woodland course. Excellent 9 holes. Red garments must be worn.

A111
A105
Lee Valley
Southgate
Palmers Green
A109
A10
A1010
A1055
A406
Muswell Hill
A1055
Hornsey
A503
Highgate
A10
Stamford Hill
Hampstead Heath
A107
A104
Leyton
Holloway
A106
A102(M)
A400
A503
A1
Hackney
A1
A501
A10
St. Pauls Cathedral
Marble Arch
Trafalgar Square
A13
LONDON
Buckingham Palace
Millennium Wheel
Houses of Parliament
A2
New Cross
Camberwell
A202
A2214
Clapham
A23
Aquarius
A205
A205
Tulse Hill
Dulwich & Sydenham
A214
Streatham
Crystal Palace
A216
A214
A23
A212

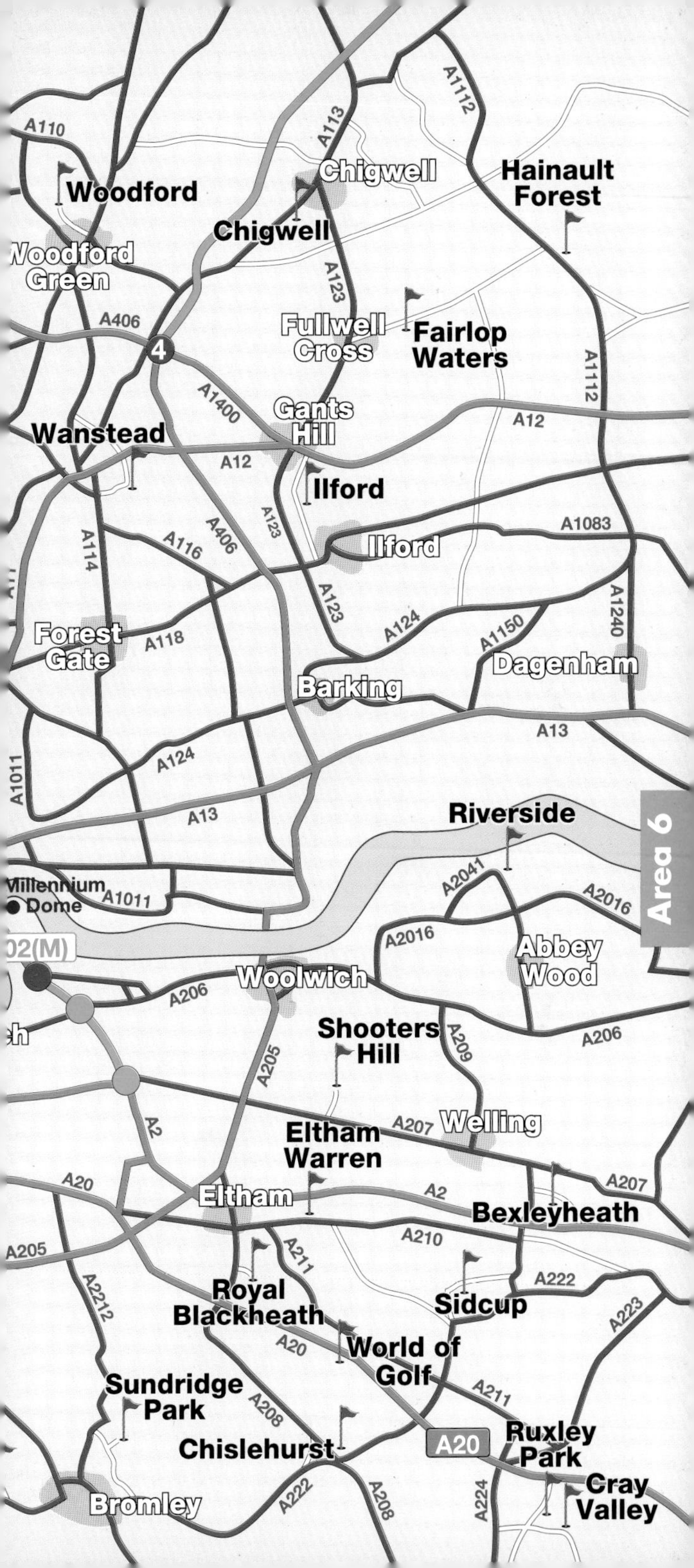

A110
Woodford
Woodford Green
Chigwell
Chigwell
A113
A1112
Hainault Forest
A123
A406
4
Fullwell Cross
Fairlop Waters
A1400
A1112
Gants Hill
A12
Wanstead
A12
Ilford
A123
A406
A116
A114
Ilford
A1083
A123
A124
A1150
A1240
Forest Gate
A118
Dagenham
Barking
A13
A124
A1011
A13
Riverside
Area 6
Millennium Dome
A1011
A2041
A2016
A2016
Abbey Wood
02(M)
Woolwich
A206
Shooters Hill
A209
A206
A205
A207
Welling
Eltham Warren
A2
A20
Eltham
A2
A207
Bexleyheath
A210
A205
A211
A222
Royal Blackheath
Sidcup
A2212
A20
World of Golf
A223
Sundridge Park
A208
A211
Chislehurst
A20
Ruxley Park
Cray Valley
A222
A208
A224
Bromley

Area Seven

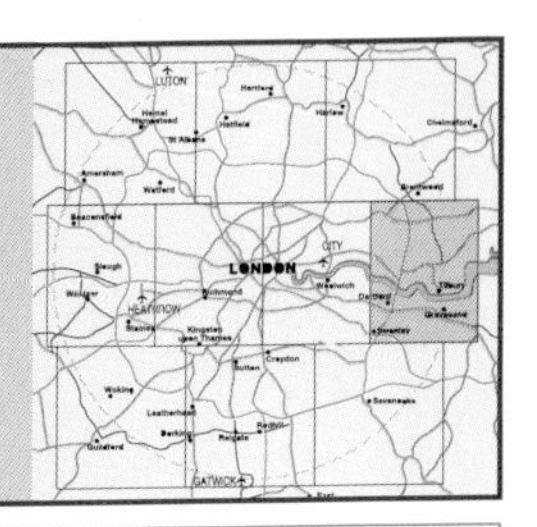

Barnehurst (1903)

Mayplace Road East, Bexleyheath, Kent DA7 6JU
Tel: 01322 552952 Fax: 554612

Green Fee: ① 9 Holes 5474 yds SSS: 68
Visitors: Any day Designer: James Braid

Pay & Play mature parkland course with easy walking.

Basildon (1967) ④

Clay Hill Lane, Basildon, Essex SS16 5JP
Tel: 01268 533297 Fax: 533849 Pro: 533352

Green Fee: ① 18 Holes 6236 yds SSS: 70
Visitors: Any day Designer: Sir Henry Cotton

Challenging undulating wooded parkland course.

Belhus Park (1972)

Belhus Road, South Ockendon, Essex RM15 4QR
Tel: 01708 854248 Fax: 854248 Pro: 854260

Green Fee: ① 18 Holes 5589 yds SSS: 69
Visitors: Any day Designer: Frank Pennink

Pay & Play part parkland/woodland course. Ideal for beginners.

Driving Range: 12 Bays, Floodlit, 6.30am-9.00pm

Birchwood Park (1990) ⑥

Birchwood Road, Wilmington, Kent DA2 7HJ
Tel: 01322 660554 Fax: 667283

Green Fee: ① 18 Holes 6364 yds SSS: 70
Visitors: Any day Designer: Howard Swann

Pleasant parkland course with wonderful views of West Kent countryside. Good test for all levels of players.

Driving Range: 38 Bays, Floodlit, 7.30am-9.30pm

The Burstead (1993)

 ④

Tye Common Road, Little Burstead, Billericay, Essex CM12 9SS
Tel: 01277 631171 Fax: 632766

Green Fee: ① 18 Holes 6275 yds SSS: 70
Visitors: Any day Designer: Patrick Tallack

Attractive colonial style clubhouse and pleasant meadowland course.

Dartford (1897)

Dartford Heath, Dartford, Kent DA1 2TN
Tel: 01322 226455 Pro: 226409

Green Fee: ① 18 Holes 5914 yds SSS: 69
Visitors: Weekdays Designer: James Braid

Heathland/Parkland course with many tree-lined fairways.

Dunton Hills (1995)

Tilbury Road, West Horndon, Nr. Brentwood, Essex CM13 3NC
Tel: 01277 812340
www.duntonhills.bizland.com

Green Fee: ① 18 Holes 6446 yds SSS: 71
Visitors: Any day Designer: Unknown

Undulating meadowland course with two lakes to cross.

Driving Range: 20 Bays, Floodlit, 9.00am-10.00pm

Hartswood (1967)

King George Playing Field, Ingrave Road, Brentwood, Essex CM14 5AE
Tel: 01277 214830 Pro: 218714

Green Fee: ① 18 Holes 6192 yds SSS: 69
Visitors: Any day Designer: Hawtree & Sons

Pay & Play flat parkland course with some ditches to cross. Many mature and quite magnificent trees.

Langdon Hills (1991)

④

Lower Dunton Road, Bulphan, Essex RM14 3TY
Tel: 01268 548444 Fax: 490084 Pro: 544300
www.greenekinggolf.co.uk

Green Fee: ① 27 Holes Langdon 3132 yds SSS: 35
Bulphan 3372 yds SSS: 37; Horndon 3054 yds SSS: 36
Visitors: Any day Designer: M. Sandow

Pleasant views of Kent and London from this modernised meadowland course.

Driving Range: 23 Bays, Floodlit, 7am-9.30pm

Maylands (1936)

⑥

Colchester Road, Harold Park, Romford, Essex RM3 0AZ
Tel: 01708 342055 Fax: 373080 Pro: 346466

Green Fee: ① 18 Holes 6361 yds SSS: 70
Visitors: Weekdays Designer: Colt/Alison/Morrison

Picturesque mixture of parkland/woodland course where Deer can often be seen.

Mid Kent (1909)

Singlewell Road, Gravesend, Kent DA11 7RB
Tel: 01474 568035 Fax: 564218 Pro: 332810

Green Fee: ① 18 Holes 6218 yds SSS: 70
Visitors: Weekdays Designer: Frank Pennink

A well-maintained and established downland course, situated close to the A2.

Orsett (1899)

⑤

Brentwood Road, Orsett, Essex RM16 3DS
Tel: 01375 891226 Fax: 892471 Pro: 891797

Green Fee: ① 18 Holes 6693 yds SSS: 72
Visitors: Weekdays Designer: James Braid

Excellent heathland course with gorse, pines, silver birch and oak trees in abundance.

Risebridge (1972)

Risebridge Chase, Lower Bedfords Road, Romford, Essex RM1 4DG
Tel: 01708 741429

Green Fee: ① 18 Holes 6271 yds SSS: 70
Visitors: Any day Designer: F. W. Hawtree

Pay & Play parkland course ideal for beginners.

Driving Range: 18 Bays, Floodlit, Dawn to dusk

Rochester & Cobham (1891)

Park Pale, by Rochester, Kent ME2 3UL
Tel: 01474 823411 Fax: 824446 Pro: 823658

Green Fee: ② 18 Holes 6596 yds SSS: 71
Visitors: Weekdays Designer: Donald Steel

One of the best inland parkland courses in Kent. Course knowledge advantages.

Romford (1894)

Heath Drive, Gidea Park, Romford, Essex RM2 5QB
Tel: 01708 740986 Fax: 752157 Pro: 749393

Green Fee: ② 18 Holes 6410 yds SSS: 70
Visitors: Weekdays Designer: Harry S. Colt

Heathland/Parkland course with many trees. Excellent test.

St. Clere's (1995)

②

London Road, Stanford-le-Hope, Essex SS17 0LX
Tel: 01375 673007 Fax: 361565 Pro: 361565

Green Fee: ① 18 Holes 6474 yds SSS: 71
Visitors: Any day Designer: Adrian Stiff

Downland course situated on a ridge of high ground with commanding views over the Thames estuary.

Driving Range: 15 Bays, Floodlit, 8.00am-10.00pm

Southern Valley (1999)

Thong Lane, Shorne, Gravesend, Kent DA12 4LF
Tel: 01474 740026 Fax: 360366 Pro: 568568

Green Fee: ① 18 Holes 6100 yds SSS: 69
Visitors: Any day Designer: Unknown

Links style course overlooking Thames Estuary with easy access from A2.

South Essex (1994)

⑳

Brentwood Road, Herongate, Essex CM13 3LW
Tel: 01277 811289
www.americangolf.com

Green Fee: ① 27 Holes Heron 3482 yds SSS: 36
Hawk 3369 yds SSS: 36 Vixon 3102 yds SSS: 36
Visitors: Any day Designer: Reg Plumbridge

Undulating meadowland course with panoramic views.

Driving Range: 14 Bays, Floodlit, 7am-10.00pm

Thorndon Park (1920)

Ingrave, Brentwood, Essex CM13 3RH
Tel: 01277 810345 Pro: 810736

Green Fee: ③ 18 Holes 6429 yds SSS: 71
Visitors: Weekdays Designer: Harry S. Colt

Considered to be the best course in Essex. Undulating parkland in delightful surroundings with glorious views.

Top Meadow (1986) ⑧

Fen Lane, North Ockendon, Essex RM14 3PR
Tel: 01708 852239 Fax: 859429 Pro: 859545

Green Fee: ① 18 Holes 6498 yds SSS: 72
Visitors: Weekdays Designer: A. Stock/D. Stock

Meadowland course with marvellous views of south Essex.

Area 7

Upminster (1928)

Hall Lane, Upminster, Essex RM14 1AU
Tel: 01708 2227889 Fax: 222484 Pro: 220000

Green Fee: ② 18 Holes 6006 yds SSS: 69
Visitors: Weekdays Designer: Harry S. Colt

Parkland course with the River Ingrebourne running through.

Warley Park (1975)

⑫

Magpie Lane, Little Warley, Brentwood, Essex CM13 3DX
Tel: 01277 224891 Fax: 200679 Pro: 200441

Green Fee: ② 27 Holes 1-9: 2988 yds Par 35
10-18: 2979 yds Par 34; 19-27: 3244 yds Par 36.
Visitors: Weekdays Designer: Reg Plumbridge

Challenging parkland course with pleasant views.

Maylands
Risebridge
28
A12
A12
Romford
A118
A127
A118
Romford
29
Warl
Park
A124
A124
Upminster
A1112
Me
A125
Rainham
M25
Belhus
Park
Sou
Ocken
30
A13
31
River Thames
A1090
Dartford
Crossing
A220
A206
A206
A282
B2186
Barnehurst
1A
A226
A226
Dartford
1b
A2
A225
A296
Dartford
A2
2
B255
Birchwood
Park
Swanley
A225
3
1

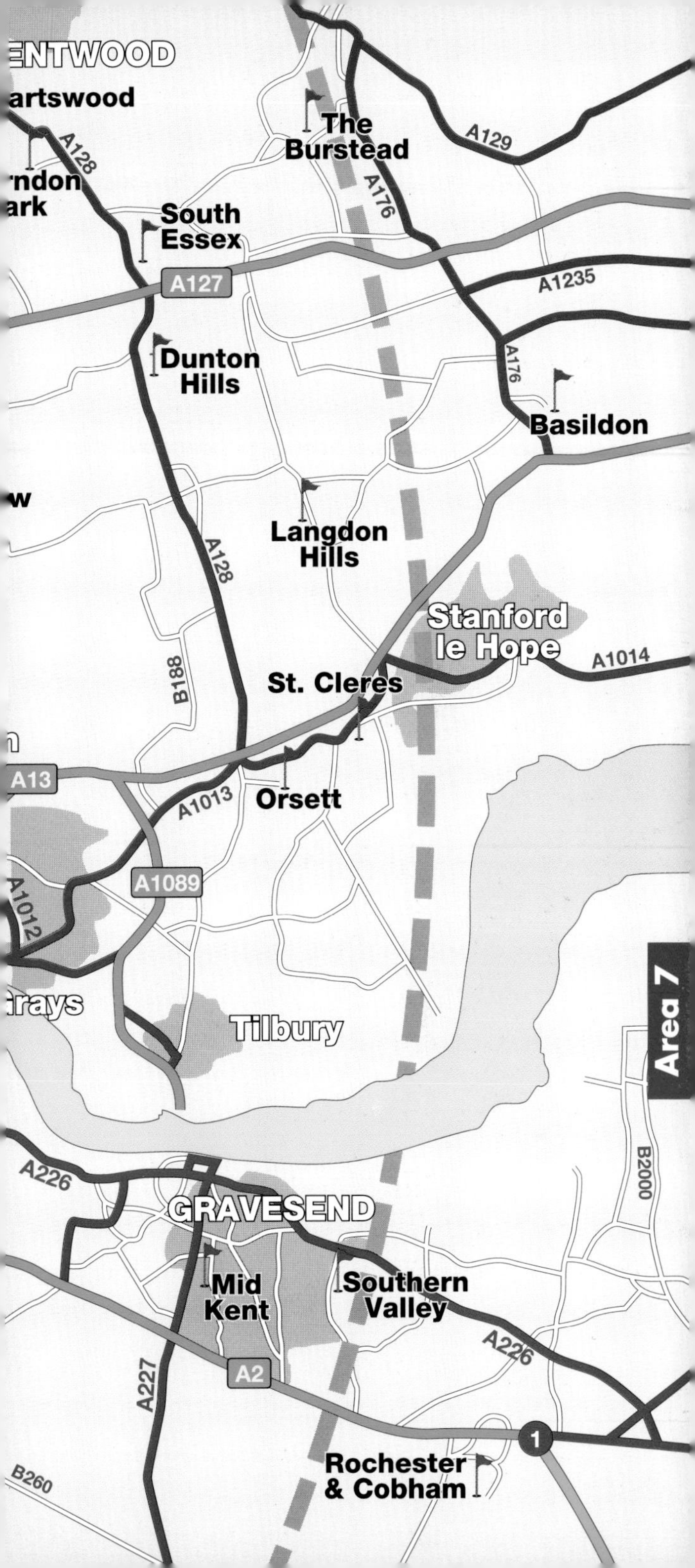

The Burstead
A129
A128
A176
South Essex
A127
A1235
Dunton Hills
A176
Basildon
Langdon Hills
A128
Stanford le Hope
A1014
B188
St. Cleres
A13
A1013
Orsett
A1089
A1012
Tilbury
Area 7
B2000
A226
GRAVESEND
Mid Kent
Southern Valley
A226
A2
A227
1
Rochester & Cobham
B260

Area Eight

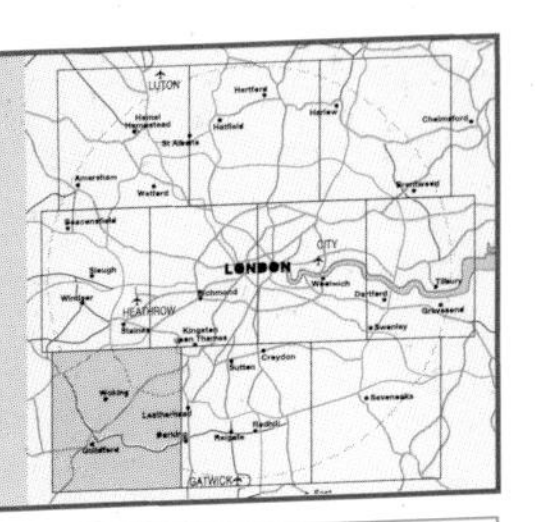

Abbey Moor (1991)

Green Lane, Addlestone, Surrey KT15 2XV
Tel: 01932 570741 or 570765

Green Fee: ① 9 Holes 5277 yds SSS: 66
Visitors: Any day Designer: David Walker

Pay & Play parkland course. Easy walking.

The Berkshire (1928) ③

Swinley Road, Ascot, Berks SL5 8AY
Tel: 01344 621495 Pro: 622351

Green Fee: ④ Red 18 Holes 6379 yds SSS: 71
Blue 18 Holes 6260 yds SSS: 71
Visitors: Weekdays Designer: Herbert Fowler

Wonderful 36 holes of heathland golf at its finest. The Red course has 6 par-3s, 6 par-4s and 6 par-5s. A gem.

Bramley (1913)  ④

Bramley, Guildford, Surrey GU5 0AL
Tel: 01483 892696 Fax: 894673 Pro: 893685

Green Fee: ② 18 Holes 5990 yds SSS: 69
Visitors: Weekdays Designer: Mayo/Braid

Parkland course with some nice views, and situated on different levels.

Burhill (1907)

Burwood Road, Walton-on-Thames. Surrey KT12 4BL
Tel: 01932 227345 Fax: 224925 Pro: 221729

Green Fee: ④ 18 Holes 6479 yds SSS: 71
Visitors: Mon to Thurs Designer: Willie Park

Parkland course set amongst some beautiful and magnificent trees. Impressive 400 year old museum is the Clubhouse. Additional 18 holes opened 2001.

Camberley Heath (1913)

 ⑮

Golf Drive, Camberley, Surrey GU15 1JG
Tel: 01276 23258 Fax: 22505 Pro: 27905

Green Fee: ③ 18 Holes 6326 yds SSS: 71
Visitors: Weekdays Designer: Harry S. Colt

One of the great heathland and heather courses in this area and now with new Clubhouse should not be missed.

Chobham (1994)

 ①

Chobham Road, Knaphill, Woking, Surrey GU21 2TU
Tel: 01276 855748 Fax: 855563 Pro: 855478
www.chobhamgolfclub,co.uk

Green Fee: ③ 18 Holes 5959 yds SSS: 69
Visitors: Weekdays Designer: Alliss/Clark

Set amongst mature oaks, this parkland/woodland course also features six man-made lakes.

Clandon Regis (1994)

Epsom Road, West Clandon, Surrey GU4 7TT
Tel: 01483 224888 Fax: 211781 Pro: 223922

Green Fee: ② 18 Holes 6412 yds SSS: 71
Visitors: Any day Designer: David Williams

High quality parkland course with challenging lake holes on back nine.

Drift (1976)

 ⑥

The Drift, East Horsley, Surrey KT24 5HD
Tel: 01483 284641 Fax: 284642 Pro: 284772

Green Fee: ② 18 Holes 6425 yds SSS: 72
Visitors: Weekdays Designer: Mr. Sandown

Picturesque woodland course with all holes tree-lined. Good straight driving advisable.

Effingham (1927)

 ②

Guildford Road, Effingham, Surrey KT24 5PZ
Tel: 01372 452203 Fax: 459959 Pro: 452606

Green Fee: ③ 18 Holes 6524 yds SSS: 71
Visitors: Weekdays Designer: Harry S. Colt

Easy walking downland and very attractive tree-lined mature course.

Fernfell (1985)

 ①

Barhatch Lane, Cranleigh, Surrey GU6 7NG
Tel: 01483 268855 Fax: 267251 Pro: 277188

Green Fee: ② 18 Holes 5648 yds SSS: 68
Visitors: Any day Designer: Unknown

Mixture of heathland and parkland.

Foxhills (1975)

 ⑮

Stone Hill Road, Ottershaw, Surrey KT16 0EL
Tel: 01932 872050 Fax: 874762 Pro: 704465
www.foxhills.co.uk

Green Fee: ② 18 Holes Bernard Hunt 6734 yds SSS: 73
18 Holes Longcross 6429 yds SSS: 72
Visitors: Any day Designer: F. W. Hawtree

Both courses are parkland with lots of fine trees, good variety of holes. Longcross is the tighter of the two courses with a premium on driving.

Area 8

Guildford (1886)

High Path Road, Merrow, Guildford, Surrey GU1 2HL
Tel: 01483 563941 Fax: 453228 Pro: 566765

Green Fee: ② 18 Holes 6090 yds SSS: 70
Visitors: Weekdays Designer: J. H. Taylor/Hawtree
Oldest course in Surrey. Rolling slopes make this downland course very interesting.

Hazelwood (1994)

Croysdale Avenue, Green Street,
Sunbury, Surrey TW16 6QU
Tel: 01932 770932 Fax: 770933
Green Fee: ① 9 Holes 5760 yds SSS: 67
Visitors: Any day Designer: Jonathan Gaunt
Pay & Play parkland course with two water features. Ideal for beginners

Hersham Village (1998)

Assher Road, Hersham, Walton on Thames,
Surrey KT12 4RA
Tel: 01932 267666 Fax: 267146
Green Fee: ① 9 Holes 6159 yds SSS: 69
Visitors: Any day Designer: Unknown
Flat parkland course with tree-lined fairways.
Driving Range: 22 Bays, Floodlit, 8.00am-9.00pm

Hoebridge (1982)

⑧

Old Woking Road, Old Woking, Surrey GU22 8JH
Tel: 01483 722611 Fax: 740369
www.hoebridge.co.uk
Green Fee: ① 18 Holes 6536 yds SSS: 71
Visitors: Any day Designer: Jacobs/Hawtree
Pay & Play parkland course. Also 9-hole and 18-hole short courses.
Driving Range: 25 Bays, Floodlit, 7.30am-10.00pm

Hurtmore (1992)

Hurtmore Road, Hurtmore, Godalming,
Surrey GU7 2RN
Tel: 01483 426492 Fax: 426121
Green Fee: ① 18 Holes 5514 yds SSS: 67
Visitors: Any day Designer: Alliss/Clark
Pay & Play course with seven lakes and over 100 bunkers.

Laleham (1903)

Laleham Reach, Chertsey, Surrey KT16 8RP
Tel: 01932 564211 Fax: 564448 Pro: 562877

Green Fee: ① 18 Holes 6211 yds SSS: 70
Visitors: Weekdays Designer: Unknown
Well bunkered flat parkland course close to the Thames with very pleasant views.

Merrist Wood (1997)

 ④

Coombe Lane, Worplesdon, Guildford, Surrey GU3 3PE
Tel: 01483 236366 Fax: 884047
www.merristwood-golfclub.co.uk

Green Fee: ③ 18 Holes 6574 yds SSS: 71
Visitors: Weekdays Designer: David Williams

Mature undulating parkland/woodland course with four large lakes and numerous streams. Panoramic views over the surrounding countryside.

Milford (1993)

 ⑪

Station Lane, Milford, Surrey GU8 5HS
Tel: 01483 419200 Fax: 419199 Pro: 416291

Green Fee: ① 18 Holes 5916 yds SSS: 68
Visitors: Any day Designer: Alliss/Clark

This meadowland course has been most interestingly designed to incorporate the surrounding trees.

Moore Place (1926)

Portsmouth Road, Esher, Surrey KT10 9LN
Tel: 01372 463533 Fax: 460274

Green Fee: ① 9 Holes 4256 yds SSS: 64
Visitors: Any day Designer: Unknown

Pay & Play undulating parkland course set in attractive surroundings.

New Zealand (1895)

③

Woodham Lane, Addlestone, Surrey KT15 3QD
Tel: 01932 345049 Fax: 342891 Pro: 349619

Green Fee: ④ 18 Holes 6012 yds SSS: 69
Visitors: Any day Designer: Muir Ferguson

Beautiful secluded heathland course set amongst heather and trees.

Pine Ridge (1992)

 ⑧

Old Bisley Road, Frimley, Camberley,
Surrey GU16 5NX
Tel: 01276 20770 Fax: 678837

Green Fee: ① 18 Holes 6458 yds SSS: 71
Visitors: Any day Designer: Clive Smith

Situated within a pine forest this Pay & Play course makes a glorious setting.

Driving Range: 36 Bays, Floodlit, 8am-10.00pm

Puttenham (1894)

Heath Road, Puttenham, Guildford, Surrey GU3 1AL
Tel: 01483 810498 Fax: 810988 Pro: 810277

Green Fee: ② 18 Holes 6214 yds SSS: 70
Visitors: Weekdays Designer: Unknown

Attractive heathland course quite tight and easy walking.

Pyrford (1993)

⑩

Warren Lane, Pyrford, Woking, Surrey GU22 8XR
Tel: 01483 723555 Fax: 729777 Pro: 751070
www.americangolf.com

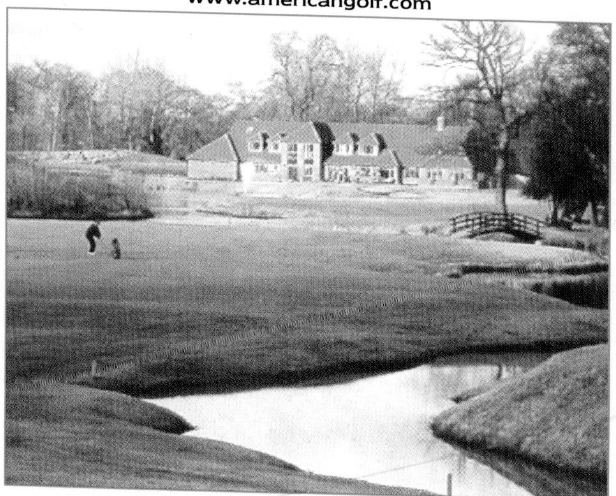

Green Fee: ③ 18 Holes 6230 yds SSS: 70
Visitors: Any day Designer: Alliss/Clark

Set next to the River Wey, this exciting inland links type course has lots of water hazards.

Queenwood (2001)

Stonehill Road, Ottershaw, Surrey KT16 0AQ
Tel: 01932 872178 Fax: 874363

Green Fee: ③ 18 Holes 6553 yds SSS: 72
Visitors: Member's Guests Designer: David McLay Kidd

A modern classic. Challenging heathland style course, abounding in heather and gorse.

Roker Park (1992)

Holly Lane, Aldershot Road, Queenswood,
Guildford, Surrey GU3 3PB
Tel: 01483 236677 Fax: 232324

Green Fee: ① 18 Holes 6074 yds SSS: 70
Visitors: Any day Designer: Alan Helling

Pay & Play 9-hole parkland course.

Driving Range: 14 Bays, Dawn to dusk

St. Georges Hill (1912)

Golf Club Road, St. Georges Hill,
Weybridge, Surrey KT13 0NL
Tel: 01932 847758 Fax: 821564 Pro: 843523

Green Fee: ④ 18 Holes 6496 yds SSS: 71
Visitors: Weekdays Designer: Harry S. Colt

Similar to Wentworth, this is another of Surrey's finest. Very undulating, this beautiful, heavily wooded course abounds with heather and rhododendrons.

Sandown Park (1970)

Moor Lane, Esher, Surrey KT10 8AN
Tel: 01372 461234

Green Fee: ① 9 Holes 5658 yds SSS: 67
Visitors: Any day Designer: John Jacobs

Pay & Play flat parkland course in middle of racecourse.

Driving Range: 33 Bays, Floodlit, 10.00am-10.00pm

Silvermere (1976)

Redhill Road, Cobham, Surrey KT11 1EF
Tel: 01932 867275 Fax: 868259 Pro: 866894
www.crowngolf.co.uk

Green Fee: ① 18 Holes 6057 yds SSS: 71
Visitors: Any day Designer: Coles/Huggett

Pay & Play parkland course with some tight driving holes.

Driving Range: 36 Bays, Floodlit, 8.00am-10.00pm

Sunbury (1993) ⑤

Charlton Lane, Sunbury, Middlesex TW17 8QA
Tel: 01932 771414 Fax: 789300 Pro: 772898
www.americangolf.com

Green Fee: ② 18 Holes 5103 yds SSS: 65
Visitors: Weekdays Designer: Unknown

Pay & Play parkland course with large lake and river in play on 6 holes.

Driving Range: 32 Bays, Floodlit, 8.00am-10.00pm

Area 8

Sunningdale (1900)

Ridgemount Road, Sunningdale, Berks. SL5 9RR
Tel: 01344 621681 Fax: 624154 Pro: 620128
www.linksnet.co.uk

Green Fee: ⑥ 36 Holes Visitors: Weekdays
Old: 6308 yds, SSS 70 Designer: Willie Park
New: 6443 yds, SSS 72 Designer: Harry S. Colt

One of Britain's finest 36 holes of marvellous heathland. These beautiful courses, possibly the most attractive in the country, should not be missed.

Sunningdale Ladies (1902)

Cross Road, Sunningdale, Berks SL5 9RX
Tel: 01344 20507

Green Fee: ① 18 Holes 3616 yds SSS: 60
Visitors: Any day Designer: Harry S. Colt

Attractive heathland course adjoining Sunningdale.

Sutton Green (1994)

 ⑥

New Lane, Sutton Green, Guildford, Surrey GU4 7QF
Tel: 01483 747898 Fax: 750289 Pro: 766849

Green Fee: ③ 18 Holes 6307 yds SSS: 70
Visitors: Any day Designer: Laura Davies

Set in undulating landscape with many testing hazards. Excellent greens and luxury clubhouse.

Swinley Forest (1909) ③

Coronation Road, Ascot, Berks. SL5 9LE
Tel: 01344 874979 Fax: 874733 Pro: 874811

Green Fee: ④ 18 Holes 6062 yds SSS: 70
Visitors: Weekdays Designer: Harry S. Colt

Beautiful heather and pine course with wonderful banks of rhododendrons.

Traditions (1999) ⑮

Pyrford Road, Pyrford, Woking, Surrey GU22 8UE
Tel: 01932 350353 Fax: 350234
www.americangolf.com

Green Fee: ① 18 Holes 6304 yds SSS: 70
Visitors: Weekdays Designer: Peter Alliss

Pay & Play with two contrasting nines, one woodland and the other lakes. Easy walking.

Wentworth (1924)  ⑩

Wentworth Drive, Virginia Water, Surrey GU25 4LS
Tel: 01344 842201 Fax: 842804 Pro: 846306
www.wentworthclub.com

West course:
Green Fee: ⑦ 18 Holes 6957 yds SSS: 74
East course:
Green Fee: ⑥ 18 Holes 6176 yds SSS: 70
Edinburgh course:
Green Fee: ⑥ 18 Holes 6979 yds SSS: 73

Designer: Harry S. Colt (East & West)
Visitors: Weekdays Designer: Jacobs/Player (Edinburgh)

Familiar from TV, this golf complex features 3 x 18 holes set amongst Surrey's finest surroundings. Heathland with pine, oak, silver birch, bracken and heather abound. Another not to be missed.

Area 8

West Byfleet (1906)

Sheerwater Road, West Byfleet, Surrey KT14 6AA
Tel: 01932 343433 Fax: 340667 Pro: 346584

Green Fee: ② 18 Holes 6211 yds SSS: 70
Visitors: Weekdays Designer: James Bluchard

Attractive woodland course with long par-4s and excellent par-3s.

West Hill (1909)

Bagshot Road, Brookwood, Surrey GU24 0BH
Tel: 01483 474365 Fax: 474252 Pro: 473172
www.surreygolf.co.uk

Green Fee: ③ 18 Holes 6368 yds SSS: 70
Visitors: Weekdays Designer: Unknown

Beautiful heathland course with lots of heather, most interesting and challenging. Five excellent short holes.

West Surrey (1910)

Enton Green, Godalming, Surrey GU8 5AF
Tel: 01483 421275 Fax: 415419 Pro: 417278

Green Fee: ③ 18 Holes 6259 yds SSS: 70
Visitors: Weekdays Designer: Herbert Fowler

Lovely parkland course in rolling wooded setting. Fairly hilly but most interesting.

Windlemere (1978)

Windlesham Road, West End, Woking, Surrey GU19 9QL
Tel: 01276 858727 Fax: 678837

Green Fee: ① 9 Holes 5346 yds SSS: 66
Visitors: Any day Designer: Clive Smith

Pay & Play, pretty course with some pleasant views.

Driving Range: 12 Bays, Floodlit, 9.00am-10.00pm

Windlesham (1994) ①

Grove End, Bagshot, Surrey GU19 5HY
Tel: 01276 452220 Fax: 452290 Pro: 451122
www.windleshamgolf.com

Green Fee: ② 18 Holes 6650 yds SSS: 72
Visitors: Any day Designer: Tommy Horton

Very fine parkland course, most interesting. Luxurious clubhouse with a John Daly length practice ground.

The Wisley (1991)

Ripley, Woking, Surrey GU23 6QU
Tel: 01344 211022 Fax: 211662 Pro: 211213

Green Fee: ③ 27 Holes
Church 3355 yds; Mill 3473 yds; Garden 3385 yds.
Visitors: Member's Guests Designer: Robert Trent Jones

Wonderful 27-hole American styled course that should be played if the opportunity arises.

Woking (1893) ②

Pond Road, Hook Heath, Woking, Surrey GU22 0JZ
Tel: 01483 760053 Fax: 772441 Pro: 769582

Green Fee: ④ 18 Holes 6340 yds SSS: 70
Visitors: Weekdays Designer: Tom Dunn

Heathland course. Bernard Darwin wrote: "The best and pleasantest place to play golf I have ever known",

Worplesdon (1908) *

Heath House Road, Woking, Surrey GU22 0RA
Tel: 01483 472277 Fax: 473303 Pro: 473287

Green Fee: ③ 18 Holes 6440 yds SSS: 71
Visitors: Weekdays Designer: J. F. Abercromby

Another wonderful heathland course, completing this magnificent triangle of 'Ws' – West Hill-Woking-Worplesdon.

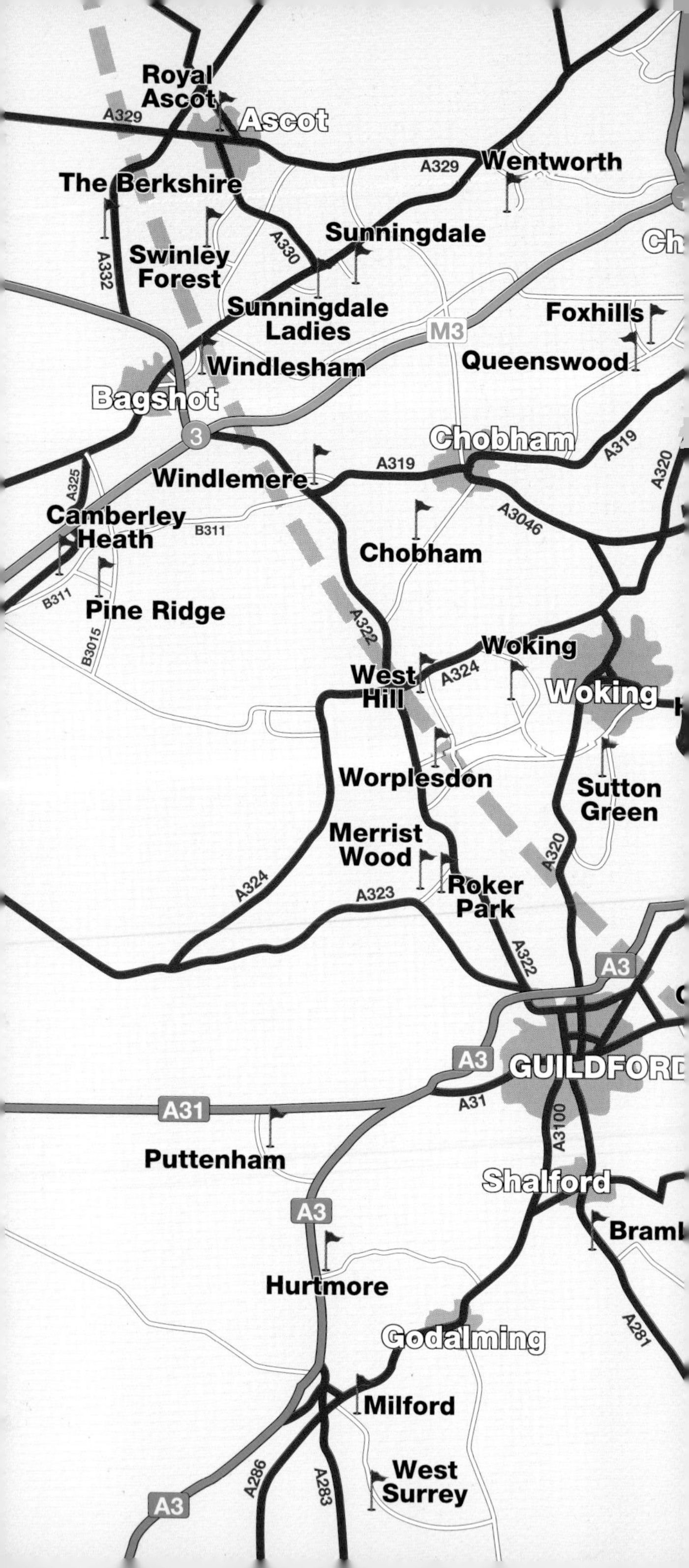
Royal Ascot
Ascot
A329
Wentworth
The Berkshire
Sunningdale
A330
A332
Swinley Forest
Sunningdale Ladies
Foxhills
M3
Queenswood
Windlesham
Bagshot
3
Chobham
A319
Windlemere
A319
A320
A325
Camberley Heath
B311
A3046
Chobham
B311
Pine Ridge
A322
B3015
Woking
West Hill
A324
Woking
Worplesdon
Sutton Green
Merrist Wood
A320
Roker Park
A324
A323
A322
A3
A3
GUILDFORD
A31
A31
A3100
Puttenham
Shalford
A3
Braml
Hurtmore
A281
Godalming
Milford
West Surrey
A286
A283
A3

Queen Mary Resr
1
A308
Hazelwood
A308
M3
R Thames
A3050
Laleham
Walton on Thames
Sunbury
R Thames
Sandown Park
Hersham Village
Abbey Moor
A317
A309
11
Weybridge
Esher
Sandown Park Race Course
A244
Moore Place
M25
St. Georges Hill
Burhill
A3
A245
Byfleet
Cobham
Silvermere
Traditions
10
A245
A3
M25
The Wisley
The Drift
Bookham
Clandon Regis
A247
A246
Effingham
A25
Shere
A25
A248
Area 8
Fernfell

Area Nine

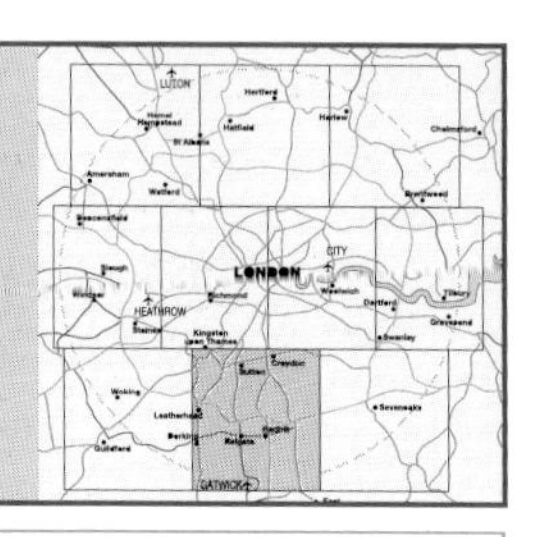

The Addington (1913)

205 Shirley Church Road, Croydon, Surrey CR0 5AB
Tel: 020 8777 6057

Green Fee: ② 18 Holes 6242 yds SSS: 71
Visitors: Weekdays Designer: J. F. Abercromby

A heathland course with heather. Many fairways tree-lined. Very challenging.

Addington Court (1931)

Featherbed Lane, Croydon, Surrey CR0 9AA
Tel: 020 8657 0281 Fax: 8651 0282
www.americangolf.com

Green Fee: ① Old 18 Holes 5577 yds SSS: 67
Falconwood 18 Holes 5513 yds SSS: 66
Visitors: Any day Designer: F. Hawtree, Snr.

Two very pleasant Pay & Play courses.

Addington Palace (1923)

Gravel Hill, Addington, Croydon, Surrey CR0 5BB
Tel: 020 8654 3061 Fax: 8655 3632 Pro: 8654 1786

Green Fee: ② 18 Holes 6410 yds SSS: 71
Visitors: Weekdays Designer: J. H. Taylor

Undulating parkland course with good interesting greens. Club house in quadrangle with putting green in Courtyard.

Banstead Downs (1890)

Burdon Lane, Belmont, Sutton, Surrey SM2 7DD
Tel: 020 8642 2284 Fax: 8642 5252 Pro: 8642 6884

Green Fee: ③ 18 Holes 6194 yds SSS: 69
Visitors: Weekdays Designer: J. Braid (6 holes 1938)

Downland course with narrow fairways and tight lies set amongst gorse. Excellent greens.

Betchworth (1913)

Reigate Road, Dorking, Surrey RH4 1NZ
Tel: 01306 882052 Fax: 877462 Pro: 884334

Green Fee: ③ 18 Holes 6266 yds SSS: 70
Visitors: Any day Designer: Harry S. Colt

Parkland course in a beautiful setting on southern ridge of Box Hill. Attractive scenery but hilly.

Area 9

Bletchingley (1993)

②

Church Lane, Bletchingley, Surrey RH1 4LP
Tel: 01883 744666 Fax: 744284 Pro: 744848
www.linksnet.co.uk

Green Fee: ① 18 Holes 6531 yds SSS: 72
Visitors: Any day Designer: Unknown

Village setting only 5 minutes from J6 of M25. Great natural wildlife habitat, several streams and ponds.

Chessington (1983)

Garrison Lane, Chessington, KT9 2LW
Tel: 020 8391 0948 Fax: 020 8397 2068

Green Fee: ① 9 Holes 3522 yds SSS: 58
Visitors: Any day Designer: Patrick Tallack

Pay & Play parkland course.

Driving Range: 18 Bays, Floodlit, 8.00am-10.00pm, W/ends, 8.00am-9.00pm

Chipstead (1906)

⑤

How Lane, Coulsdon, Surrey CR5 3PR
Tel: 01737 555781 Fax: 555404 Pro: 554939

Green Fee: ① 18 Holes 5491 yds SSS: 67
Visitors: Weekdays Designer: Unknown

Parkland course with panoramic views.

Coombe Hill (1911)

 ⑩

Golf Club Drive, Kingston-on-Thames,
Surrey KT2 7DF

Tel: 020 8942 2284 Fax: 8336 7601 Pro: 8949 3713

Green Fee: ④ 18 Holes 6293 yds SSS: 71
Visitors: Weekdays Designer: J. F. Abercromby

A beautiful tree-lined course over sloped terrain with lots of magenta rhododendrons.

Coombe Wood (1904)

George Road, Kingston Hill, Kingston-on-Thames,
Surrey KT2 7NS

Tel: 020 8942 0388 Fax: 8942 0388 Pro: 8942 6764

Green Fee: ② 18 Holes 5299 yds SSS: 66
Visitors: Weekdays Designer: Mr. Williamson

Parkland course. Short but fairly difficult. Couple of excellent par-3s.

Coulsdon Manor (1937)

 ④

Coulsdon Court Road, Coulsdon, Surrey CR5 2LL

Tel: 020 8668 0414 Fax: 8668 3118 Pro: 8660 6083

Green Fee: ① 18 Holes 6037 yds SSS: 68
Visitors: Any day Designer: Harry S. Colt

Public parkland course attached to Coulsdon Manor Hotel.

Croham Hurst (1911)

Croham Road, South Croydon, Surrey CR2 7HJ

Tel: 020 8657 5581 Fax: 8657 3229 Pro: 8657 7705

Green Fee: ③ 18 Holes 6290 yds SSS: 70
Visitors: Weekdays Designer: Unknown

Parkland course known for its good condition and some nice views.

Area 9

Cuddington (1929)

Banstead Road, Banstead, Surrey SM7 1RD
Tel: 020 8393 0952 Fax: 8786 7025 Pro: 8393 5850

Green Fee: ③ 18 Holes 6595 yds SSS: 71
Visitors: Any day Designer: Harry S. Colt

Parkland tree-lined course with wonderful view from clubhouse. New USGA greens opened in 2000. Excellent drainage provides first class winter golf

Dorking (1897)

Chart Park, Deepdene Avenue, Dorking, Surrey RH5 4BX
Tel: 01306 886917 Fax: 886917

Green Fee: ① 9 Holes 5163 yds SSS: 65
Visitors: Weekdays Designer: James Braid

Undulating parkland course, short but difficult with many mature trees and nice views.

Dukes Dene (1996)

⑥

Slines New Road, Woldingham, Surrey CR3 7HA
Tel: 01883 653501 Fax: 653502 Pro: 653541
www.clubhaus.com.

Green Fee: ② 18 Holes 6393 yds SSS: 71
Visitors: Weekdays Designer: Bradford Benz

Set in the Halliloo Valley. Interesting course with wonderful facilities.

Epsom Downs (1889)

Longdown Lane South, Epsom, Surrey KT17 4JR
Tel: 01372 721666 Fax: 817183 Pro: 741867

Green Fee: ① 18 Holes 5701 yds SSS: 69
Visitors: Any day Designer: Unknown

Downland course on common land. Not long but difficult to score well. Adjacent to Epsom Racecourse.

Farleigh Court (1997)

Old Farleigh Road, Farleigh, Surrey CR6 9PX
Tel: 01883 627711 Fax: 627722

Green Fee: ② 18 Holes 6409 yds SSS: 71
9 Holes 3281 yds SSS: 36
Visitors: Any day Designer: John Jacobs

Surrounded by forest and bird sanctuary. Excellent clubhouse.

Happy Valley (1999)

⑯

Rook Lane, Chaldon, Nr. Caterham, Surrey CR3 5AA
Tel: 01883 344555 Fax: 344422
www.happyvalley.co.uk

Green Fee: ① 18 Holes 6612 yds SSS: 72
Visitors: Any day Designer: David Williams

Meadowland course running through two valleys, creating challenging play.

Home Park (1895)

Hampton Wick, Kingston-on-Thames, Surrey KT1 4AD
Tel: 020 8977 2423 Fax: 8977 4414 Pro: 8977 2658

Green Fee: ① 18 Holes 6584 yds SSS: 71
Visitors: Any day Designer: Unknown

Mainly parkland course. Hampton Court Palace adjacent. Also home to herd of fallow deer.

Horne Park (1995)

Croydon Barn Lane, Horne, South Godstone, Surrey RH9 8JP
Tel: 01342 844443 Fax: 844715
www.surreygolf.co.uk

Green Fee: ① 9 Holes 5436 yds SSS: 66
Visitors: Any day Designer: H. Swan

Meadowland course.

Driving Range: 23 Bays, 9.00am-Dusk

Horton Park (1993) ③

Hook Road, Epsom, Surrey KT19 8QG
Tel: 020 8393 8400 Fax: 8394 1369 Pro: 8394 2626

Green Fee: ① 18 Holes 5208 yds SSS: 65
Visitors: Any day Designer: Patrick Tallack

Pay & Play parkland course.

Driving Range: 26 Bays, Floodlit, 8.00am-9.30pm

Kingswood (1928) ⑧

Sandy Lane, Kingswood, Tadworth,
Surrey KT20 6NE
Tel: 01737 832188 Fax: 833920 Pro: 832334

Green Fee: ③ 18 Holes 6904 yds SSS: 73
Visitors: Any day Designer: James Braid

Flat but very testing parkland course. Always in excellent condition.

Leatherhead (1903) ⑥

Kingston Road, Leatherhead, Surrey KT22 0EE
Tel: 01372 843966 Fax: 842241 Pro: 843956
www.lgc-golf.co.uk

Green Fee: ③ 18 Holes 6203 yds SSS: 70
Visitors: Weekdays Designer: Unknown

Attractive parkland course with many trees. Numerous ditches throughout.

Lingfield Park (1987)

Racecourse Road, Lingfield, Surrey RH7 8PQ
Tel: 01342 834602 Fax: 836077 Pro: 832659

Green Fee: ③ 18 Holes 6487 yds SSS: 72
Visitors: Any day Designer: Unknown

Challenging tree-lined parkland course with ponds and streams throughout.

Driving Range: 15 Bays, Dawn to dusk.

Malden (1893)

④

Traps Lane, New Malden, Surrey KT3 4RS
Tel: 020 8942 0654 Fax: 8336 2219 Pro: 8942 6009

Green Fee: ② 18 Holes 6295 yds SSS: 70
Visitors: Weekdays Designer: Unknown

Parkland course. Easy walking. Beverley Brook runs through the course.

Mitcham (1897)

Carshalton Road, Mitcham, Surrey CR4 4HN
Tel: 020 8648 4197 Fax: 8648 4197 Pro: 8640 4280

Green Fee: ① 18 Holes 5935 yds SSS: 68
Visitors: Any day Designer: Tom Morris

Pay & Play course on common land. Very challenging with super greens.

North Downs (1899)

②

Northdown Road, Woldingham, Surrey CR3 7AA
Tel: 01883 652057 Fax: 652832 Pro: 653004

Green Fee: ① 18 Holes 5843 yds SSS: 68
Visitors: Weekdays Designer: Unknown

Downland course with fine views. Quite hilly.

Oaks Park (1973)

②

Woodmansterne Road, Carshalton, Surrey SM5 4AN
Tel: 020 8643 8363 Fax: 8770 7303

Green Fee: ① 18 Holes 5975 yds SSS: 69
Visitors: Any day Designer: Unknown

Pay & Play meadowland course. Also 9-hole par-3 course.

Driving Range: 16 Bays, Floodlit, 9.00am-10.00pm

Pachesham Park (1990)

Oaklawn Road, Leatherhead, Surrey KT22 0BT
Tel: 01372 843453 Fax: 01372 844076

Green Fee: ① 9 Holes 5608 yds SSS: 67
Visitors: Any day Designer: Philip Taylor

Pay & Play parkland course.

Driving Range: 33 Bays, Floodlit, 9.00am-9.30pm

Purley Downs (1894)

④

106 Purley Downs Road, South Croydon, Surrey CR2 0RB
Tel: 020 8657 8347 Fax: 8651 5044 Pro: 8651 0819

Green Fee: ② 18 Holes 6275 yds SSS: 70
Visitors: Weekdays Designer: J. H. Taylor

Attractive hilly downland course.

RAC Country Club (1913)

Woodcote Park, Epsom, Surrey KT18 7EW
Tel: 01372 276311 Fax: 276117 Pro: 279514

Green Fee: ② Old: 18 Holes 6709 yds SSS: 72
Coronation: 18 Holes 5644 yds SSS: 67
Visitors: Member's Guests Designer: Unknown

Two courses over undulating downland. Stunning clubhouse with usual country club facilities.

Redhill Golf Centre (1993)

Canada Avenue, Redhill, Surrey RH1 5BF
Tel: 01737 770204 Fax: 760046

Green Fee: ① 9 Holes 3806 yds SSS: 62
Visitors: Any day Designer: Unknown

Pay & Play. Ideal for beginners.

Driving Range: 37 Bays, Floodlit, 8.00am-10.00pm

Redhill and Reigate (1887)

Clarence Lodge, Pendleton Road, Redhill, Surrey RH1 6LB
Tel: 01737 240777 Pro: 244433

Green Fee: ① 18 Holes 5272 yds SSS: 66
Visitors: Any day Designer: James Braid

Tree-lined course set around lakes and wooded area.

Reigate Heath (1895)

Flanchford Road, Reigate, Surrey RH2 8QR
Tel: 01737 226793
www.surreygolf.co.uk

Green Fee: ① 18 Holes 5658 yds SSS: 67
Visitors: Weekdays Designer: Unknown

Very beautiful heathland course set amongst heather, silver birch and pine trees.

Reigate Hill (1995) ④

Gatton Bottom, Reigate, Surrey RH2 0TU
Tel: 01737 645577 Fax: 642650 Pro: 646070

Green Fee: ② 18 Holes 6175 yds SSS: 70
Visitors: Any day Designer: David Williams

Partly hilly meadowland course with some very interesting golf holes, testing undulating greens. Well worth a visit.

Selsdon Park Hotel (1929)  ⑳

Addington Road, Sanderstead, Croydon, Surrey CR2 8YA
Tel: 020 8657 8811 Fax: 8651 6171 Pro: 8657 4129

Green Fee: ② 18 Holes 6473 yds SSS: 71
Visitors: Any day Designer: J. H. Taylor

Challenging downland course adjoining Selsdon Park Hotel, with Golf Academy for practice.

Shirley Park (1914)

194 Addiscombe Road, Croydon, Surrey CR0 7LB
Tel: 020 8654 1143 Fax: 8654 6733 Pro: 8654 8767

Green Fee: ② 18 Holes 6210 yds SSS: 70
Visitors: Weekdays Designer: Unknown

Parkland course. The short 7th is a particularly challenging and picturesque hole.

Surbiton (1895)

Woodstock Lane, Chessington, Surrey KT9 1UG
Tel: 020 8398 3101 Fax: 8339 0992 Pro: 8398 6619

Green Fee: ② 18 Holes 6055 yds SSS: 69
Visitors: Weekdays Designer: Tom Dunn

Pleasant undulating parkland course with scenic views. Well established with many wooded areas.

Tandridge (1925)

Oxted, Surrey RH8 9NQ
Tel: 01883 712274 Fax: 730537 Pro: 713701

Green Fee: ③ 18 Holes 6250 yds SSS: 70
Visitors: Mon-Wed-Thur Designer: Harry S. Colt

Although flattish over front nine, this rolling parkland course has an undulating back nine with excellent views.

Thames Ditton & Esher (1892)

Portsmouth Road, Esher, Surrey KT10 9AL
Tel: 020 8398 1551

Green Fee: ① 9 Holes 5149 yds SSS: 65
Visitors: Any day Designer: Unknown

Common heathland course like inland links. Renowned for winter greens.

Tyrrells Wood (1924)

Tyrrells Wood, Leatherhead, Surrey KT22 8QP
Tel: 01372 376026 Fax: 360836 Pro: 375200

Green Fee: ③ 18 Holes 6310 yds SSS: 70
Visitors: Weekdays Designer: James Braid

Excellent parkland course. Very mature but quite hilly.

Walton Heath (1903)

Deans Lane, Walton-on-the-Hill, Tadworth, Surrey KT20 7TP
Tel: 01737 812380 Fax: 814225 Pro: 812152
www.whgc.co.uk

Green Fee: ④ Old: 18 Holes 6817 yds SSS: 73
New: 18 Holes 6613 yds SSS: 72
Visitors: Weekdays Designer: H. W. Fowler

One of Surreys finest heathland courses. 36 holes, featuring heather, gorse, pine, birch and oak.

Woodcote Park (1912)

Meadow Hill, Bridle Way, Coulsdon, Surrey CR5 2QQ
Tel: 020 8668 2788 Fax: 8668 2788 Pro: 8668 1843

Green Fee: ② 18 Holes 6669 yds SSS: 72
Visitors: Weekdays Designer: Unknown

Undulating parkland course.

Kingston
Coombe Hill
Coombe Wood
Malden
Home Park
River Thames
World of Golf
Thames Ditton
Surbiton
Horton Park
Sutton
Banstead Downs
Chessington
Cuddington
Epsom
Leatherhead
RAC
Epsom Downs
Banstead
Pachesham Park
Epsom
Tyrrells Wood
Kingswoo
Walton Heath
Reig Hi
Betchworth
Reigate Heath
Dorking
Reigate
Redh & Reig
Dorking
Gatwick
A24
A2043
A240
A243
A3
A232
B284
B280
B2218
B2230
A2022
B2219
A217
B2032
B2220
B2033
A246
M25
A2003
A25
A29
9
8

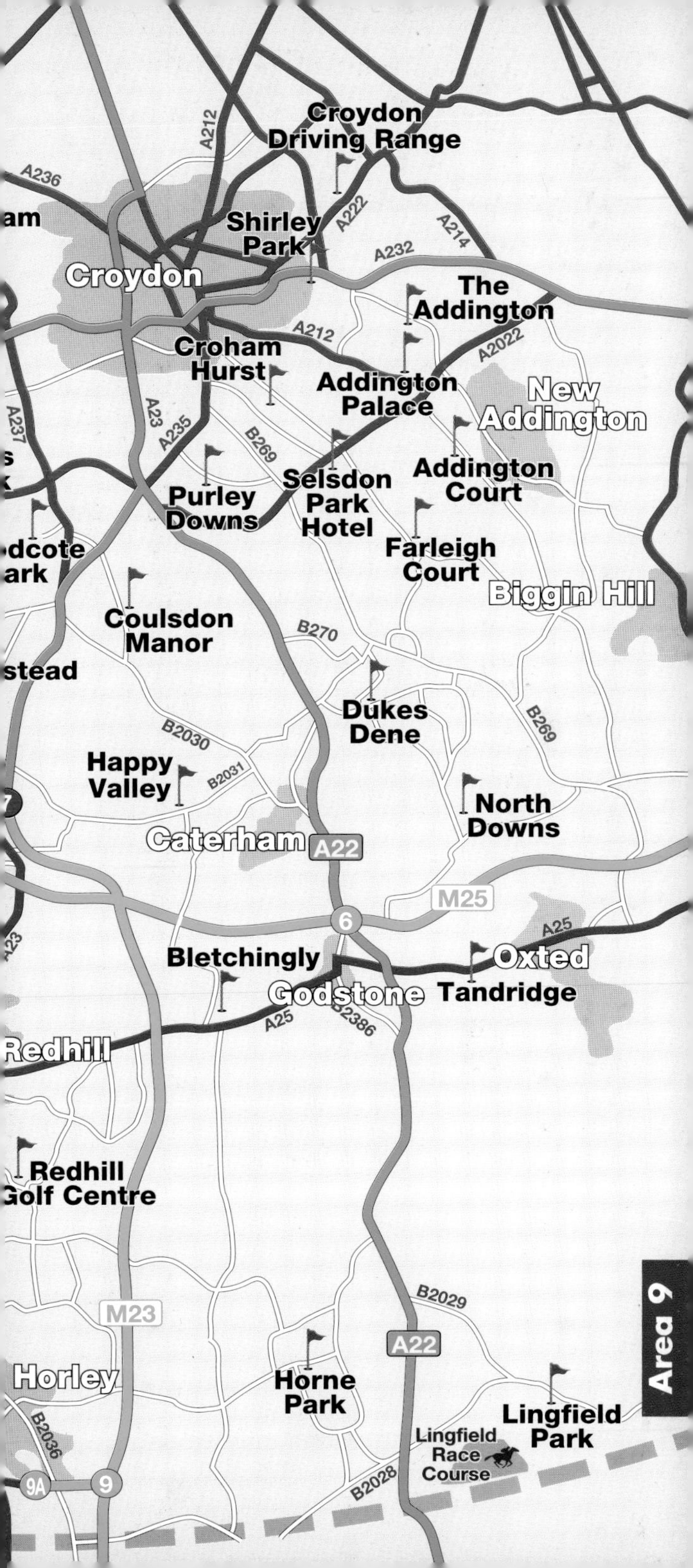
Croydon Driving Range
Shirley Park
Croydon
A236
A212
A222
A214
A232
The Addington
A212
A2022
Croham Hurst
Addington Palace
New Addington
A23
A235
B269
A237
Purley Downs
Selsdon Park Hotel
Addington Court
Farleigh Court
Biggin Hill
Coulsdon Manor
B270
Dukes Dene
B269
B2030
Happy Valley
B2031
North Downs
Caterham
A22
M25
6
A25
Bletchingly
Oxted
Tandridge
Godstone
A25
B2386
Redhill
Redhill Golf Centre
B2029
M23
A22
Horne Park
Lingfield Park
Horley
Lingfield Race Course
B2036
B2028
9A
9
Area 9

Area Ten

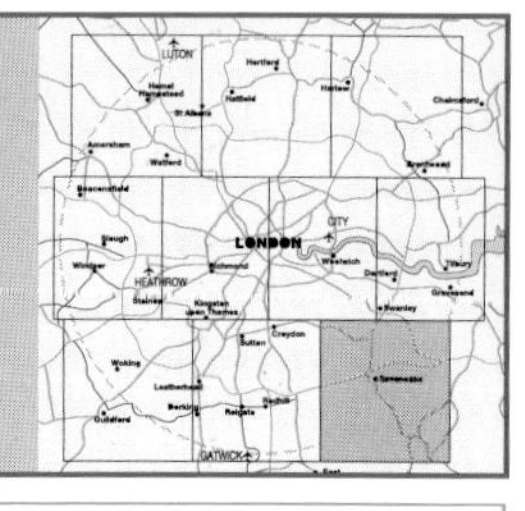

Austin Lodge (1991)

20+

Upper Austin Lodge Road, Eynsford, Kent DA4 0HU
Tel: 01322 868944 Fax: 862406 Pro: 863000

Green Fee: ① 18 Holes 6575 yds SSS: 71
Visitors: Any day Designer: Peter Bevan

Lies naturally in three secluded valleys in rolling countryside.

Broke Hill (1993)

Sevenoaks Road, Halstead, Kent TN14 7HR
Tel: 01959 533225 Fax: 532680 Pro: 533810

Green Fee: ② 18 Holes 6374 yds SSS: 71
Visitors: Weekdays Designer: David Williams

Parkland course. At over 500ft, there are some pleasant views. Friendly club. Visitors are welcome.

Bromley (1948)

Magpie Hall Lane, Bromley, Kent BR2 8JF
Tel: 020 8462 7014

Green Fee: ① 9 Holes 5490 yds SSS: 67
Visitors: Any day Designer: Unknown

Pay & Play. Ideal course for beginners, everyone made very welcome.

Chartham Park (1993)

Felcourt Road, East Grinstead, Sussex RH19 2JT
Tel: 01342 870340 Fax: 870719
www.americangolf.com

Green Fee: ② 18 Holes 6680 yds SSS: 72
Visitors: Any day Designer: Neil Coles

Very mature parkland course in the grounds of an old stately home.

Chelsfield Lakes (1992)

Court Road, Orpington, Kent BR6 9BX
Tel: 01689 896266 Fax: 824577

Green Fee: ① 18 Holes 6110 yds SSS: 69
Visitors: Any day Designer: M. R. M. Sandow

Pay & Play over downland. The course offers commanding views of the countryside. Well equipped shop.

Driving Range: 40 Bays, Floodlit, 7am-9.30pm

Cherry Lodge (1969) ④

Jail Lane, Biggin Hill, Kent TN16 3AX
Tel: 01959 572250 Fax: 540672 Pro: 572989

Green Fee: ② 18 Holes 6652 yds SSS: 73
Visitors: Weekdays Designer: John Day

Situated in the heart of the Kent countryside, this challenging parkland course has many pleasant views.

Darenth Valley (1972)

Station Road, Shoreham, Sevenoaks, Kent TN14 7SA
Tel: 01959 522944 Fax: 525089 Pro: 522922

Green Fee: ① 18 Holes 6327 yds SSS: 71
Visitors: Any day Designer: M. Cross

Pay & Play parkland course in scenic Darenth Valley. Situated adjacent to Shoreham village. Easy reach of M25.

Edenbridge (1973) ⑥

Crouch House Road, Edenbridge, Kent TN8 5LQ
Tel: 01732 867381 Fax: 867029 Pro; 865097

Green Fee: ① Old: 18 Holes 6577 yds SSS: 72
New: 18 Holes 5605 yds SSS: 67
Visitors: Any day Designer: Unknown

Set in beautiful parkland, this undulating Pay & Play course is challenging to golfers of every standard.

Driving Range: 16 Bays, Floodlit, 7.00am-8.30pm

Fawkham Valley (1987)

⑥

Gay Dawn Farm, Fawkham, Longfield, Kent DA3 8LZ
Tel: 01474 707144 Fax: 707911
www.fawkhamvalley.co.uk

Green Fee: ① 9 Holes 6547 yds SSS: 72
Visitors: Any day Designer: Golf Landscapes

A 9-hole parkland course.

Hever (1993)

⑮

Hever, near Edenbridge, Kent TN8 7NP
Tel: 01732 700771 Fax: 700775
www.hever.com

Green Fee: ③ 18 Holes 7002 yds SSS: 75
Visitors: Any day Designer: Peter Nicholson

A parkland course with thousands of mature trees in one of the prettiest locations in England. Water in play on ten holes. Adjacent to Hever Castle.

High Elms (1969)

⑧

High Elms Road, Downe, Orpington, Kent BR6 7JL
Tel: 01689 858175

Green Fee: ① 18 Holes 6209 yds SSS: 70
Visitors: Any day Designer: Unknown

This Pay & Play wooded parkland course is a good society venue. The par-3 13th 224yd is one of the best holes.

Hilden Golf Centre (1994)

Rings Hill, Hildenborough, Kent TN11 8LX
Tel: 01732 834404 Fax: 834484 Pro: 833607

Green Fee: ① 9 Holes 3114 yds SSS: 60
Visitors: Any day Designer: Unknown

Pay & Play 9-hole executive Course.

Driving Range: 40 Bays, Floodlit, 8.00am-10.00pm

Holtye (1893)

Cowden, Edenbridge, Kent TN8 7ED
Tel: 01342 850576 Fax: 850576 Pro: 850635

Green Fee: ① 9 Holes 5325 yds SSS: 66
Visitors: Weekdays Designer: Unknown

Nine delightful holes of heath and heather. Excellent greens and drainage make this an all-year-round course.

Knole Park (1924)

Seal Hollow Road, Sevenoaks, Kent TN15 0HJ
Tel: 01732 452709 Fax: 463159 Pro: 451740

Green Fee: ③ 18 Holes 6238 yds SSS: 70
Visitors: Weekdays Designer: J. F. Abercromby

A most beuatiful woodland course over natural contours of land. Park deer roam. Marvellous views.

Langley Park (1910)

Barnfield Wood Road, Beckenham, Kent BR3 6SZ
Tel: 020 8650 2090 Fax: 8658 6310 Pro: 8650 1663

Green Fee: ③ 18 Holes 6488 yds SSS: 71
Visitors: Weekdays Designer: J. H. Taylor

Relatively flat, parkland course with tree-lined fairways. Eight par-4 holes of over 400 yards. 18th is a par-3 played over a lake.

Limpsfield Chart (1889)

Westerham Road, Limpsfield Chart, Surrey RH8 0SL
Tel: 01883 723405

Green Fee: ① 9 Holes 5718 yds SSS: 68
Visitors: Any day Designer: Unknown

Tight heathland course. Well wooded and set in National Trust land.

London Club (1993)

 ⑫

Stanstead Lane, Ash Green, Sevenoaks, Kent TN15 7EN
Tel: 01474 879899 Fax: 879912
www.londongolf.co.uk

Green Fee: ② Visitors:Member's Guests
Heritage: 18 Holes 6771 yds SSS: 72
Inter: 18 Holes 6574 yds SSS: 71
Designer: Jack Nicklaus (Heritage)
Ron Kirby (International)

This 36-hole complex with superb clubhouse maintains the highest standards. A special day to be remembered.

Lullingstone (1967)

 ⑱

Parkgate Road, Chelsfield, Orpington, Kent BR6 7PX
Tel: 01959 533793 Fax: 533795

Green Fee: ① 18 Holes 6779 yds SSS: 72
Visitors: Any day Designer: Unknown

Pay & Play. Undulating parkland course situated within the beautiful surroundings of Lullingstone Park.

Moatlands (1993)

 ⑳

Watermans Lane, Brenchley, Kent TN12 6ND
Tel: 01892 724400 Fax: 723300 Pro: 724252

Green Fee: ② 18 Holes 6693 yds SSS: 72
Visitors: Any day Designer: K. Saito

Rolling parkland course with marvellous views over Weald of Kent. Challenging and interesting layout.

Nizels (1992)

Nizels Lane, Hildenborough, Kent TN11 8NU
Tel: 01732 833138 Fax: 833764 Pro: 838926
www.americangolf.com

Green Fee: ③ 18 Holes 6297 yds SSS: 71
Visitors: Weekdays Designer: Lenman/Purnell

Woodland course with mature trees and lakes. Panoramic views. Clubhouse has excellent faciiities.

Park Wood (1994)

Chestnut Avenue, Westerham, Kent TN16 2EG
Tel: 01959 577744 Fax: 572002 Pro: 577177

Green Fee: ③ 18 Holes 6835 yds SSS: 72
Visitors: Any day Designer: Les Smith

On top of North Downs Ridge. Marvellous views. Highest point in Kent. Parkland course with water hazards.

Pedham Place (1996)

London Road, Swanley, Kent BR8 8PP
Tel: 01322 867000 Fax: 861646
www.ppgc.co.uk

Green Fee: ① 9 Holes 5564 yds SSS: 67
Visitors: Any day Designer: John Fortune

Pay & Play meadowland course adjacent to M25.

Driving Range: 40 Bays, Floodlit, 8.00am-10.00pm

Poult Wood (1974)

Higham Lane, Tonbridge, Kent TN11 9QR
Tel: 01732 366180 Pro: 364039

Green Fee: ① 18 Holes 5569 yds SSS: 67
Visitors: Any day Designer: Unknown

Pay & Play parkland course with water hazards. Easy walking. Although short it is still a good test. Also has 9-hole short course.

Redlibbets (1996) ③

Manor Lane, West Yoke, Ash, Sevenoaks, Kent TN15 7HJ
Tel: 01474 879190 Fax: 879290 Pro: 872278
www.golfandsport.co.uk

Green Fee: ② 18 Holes 6636 yds SSS: 72
Visitors: Weekdays Designer: Jonathan Gaunt

Built around and through picturesque valley, this new course is situated in over 150 acres of undulating parkland and woodland with hundreds of mature trees.

Sweetwoods Park (1994)

 ⑩

Cowden, Edenbridge, Kent TN8 7JN
Tel: 01342 850942 Fax: 850866 Pro: 850729

Green Fee: ① 18 Holes 6512 yds SSS: 71
Visitors: Any day Designer: Peter Strand

Undulating parkland course. Lots of water. Mature beyond its age.

Tunbridge Wells (1889)

Langton Road, Tunbridge Wells, Kent TN4 8XH
Tel: 01892 536918 Pro: 541386

Green Fee: ① 9 Holes 4560 yds SSS: 62
Visitors: Any day Designer: Unknown

Hilly picturesque meadowland course. Well bunkered with lake.

Westerham (1997)

 ⑯

Valence Park, Brasted Road, Westerham, Kent TN16 1LJ
Tel: 01959 567100 Fax: 567101

Green Fee: ② 18 Holes 6272 yds SSS: 70
Visitors: Weekdays Designer: David Williams

While part parkland, the majority of the course is played down tree-lined fairways. Greens laid to USGA standards. Some very pleasant views of the Kent countryside.

West Kent (1916)

 ②

West Hill, Downe, Orpington, Kent BR6 7JJ
Tel: 01689 851323 Fax: 858693 Pro: 856863

Green Fee: ② 18 Holes 6399 yds SSS: 70
Visitors: Weekdays Designer: Unknown

Parkland/Heathland course over undulating ground. Well wooded with heather and gorse.

West Malling (1974)

 ⑫

London Road, Addington, Maidstone, Kent ME19 5AR
Tel: 01732 844785 Fax: 844795 Pro: 844022

Green Fee: ② Spitfire: 18 Holes 6142 yds SSS: 70
Hurricane: 18 Holes 6011 yds SSS: 69
Visitors: Any day Designer: Max Faulkner

Two 18-hole parkland courses enjoying mature trees and natural lakes.

Wildernesse (1890)

 ②

Park Lane, Seal, Sevenoaks, Kent TN15 0JE
Tel: 01732 761199 Fax: 761389 Pro: 761527

Green Fee: ② 18 Holes 6448 yds SSS: 72
Visitors: Weekdays Designer: Unknown

Fine, tight inland course, heavily wooded with fine tree-lined fairways. Few slopes and easy walking.

Woodlands Manor (1925)

 ③

Woodlands, Tinkerpot Lane, Sevenoaks, Kent TN15 6AB
Tel: 01959 523805 Pro: 524161

Green Fee: ① 18 Holes 6037 yds SSS: 68
Visitors: Weekdays Designer: Coles/Lyons

Hilly course with stunning views. Water features on the course. This woodland course is a real challenge.

Wrotham Heath (1906)

Seven Mile Lane, Borough Green, Kent TN15 8QZ
Tel: 01732 884800 Pro: 883854

Green Fee: ② 18 Holes 5954 yds SSS: 69
Visitors: Weekdays Designer: Donald Steel

Heathland and woodland course with excellent views over the North Downs. Very pretty. Soil conditions are sandy with excellent drainage.

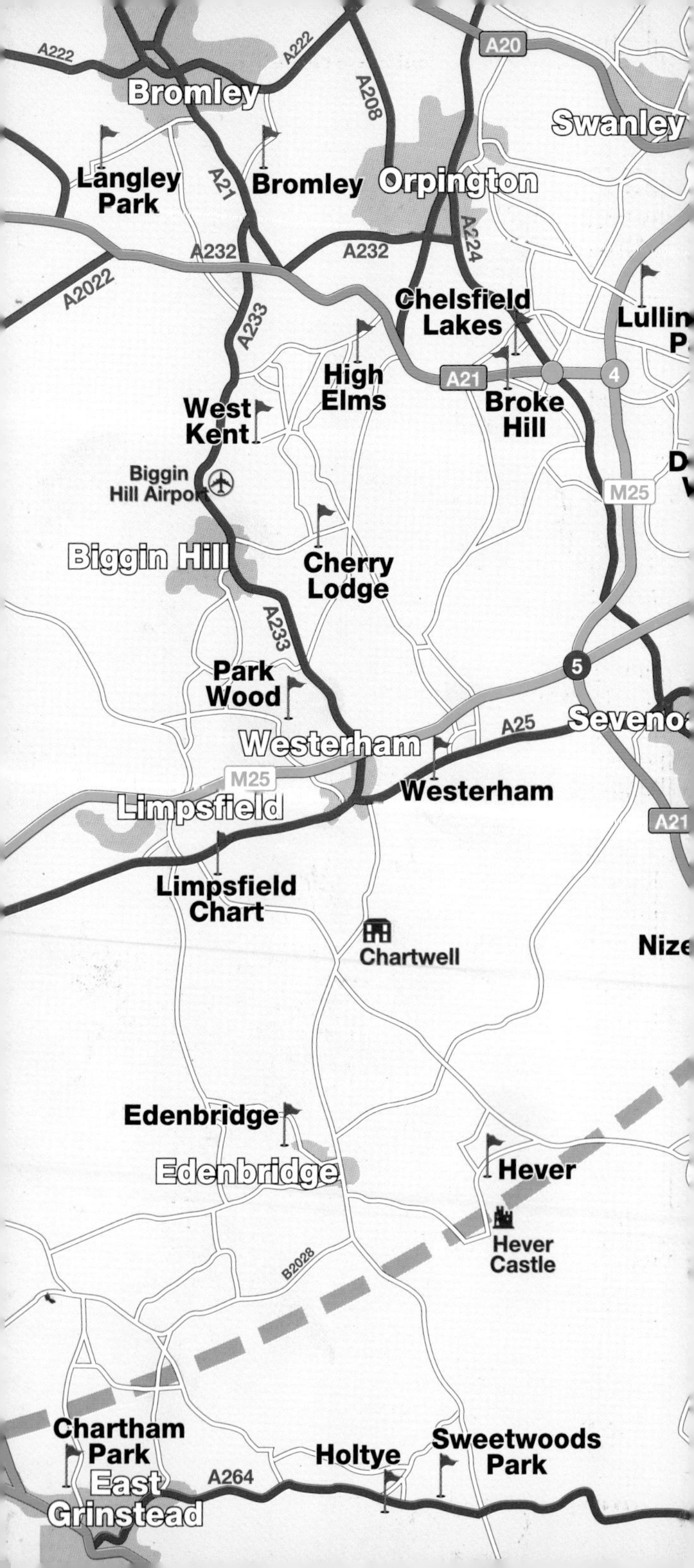
A222
A222
A20
Bromley
A208
Swanley
Langley
Park
A21
Bromley
Orpington
A224
A232
A232
A2022
Chelsfield
Lakes
A233
High
Elms
A21
4
Broke
Hill
West
Kent
Biggin
Hill Airport
M25
Biggin Hill
Cherry
Lodge
A233
5
Park
Wood
A25
Westerham
Westerham
M25
Limpsfield
A21
Limpsfield
Chart
Chartwell
Edenbridge
Edenbridge
Hever
Hever
Castle
B2028
Chartham
Park
Holtye
Sweetwoods
Park
East
Grinstead
A264